THE BOTANISTS
AND GUIDES
OF SNOWDONIA

I D. C. a E. Lewthwaite
gyda phob dymuniad da.
Dewi Jones, Tachwedd 1996.

The Botanists and Guides of Snowdonia

Dewi Jones

ISBN: 0-86381-383-6

Cover photo:
Old print of Snowdon Summit
during 1850's

Print on title page courtesy of
National Library of Wales.

First published in 1996 by Gwasg Carreg Gwalch,
12 Iard yr Orsaf, Llanrwst, Wales LL26 0EH
☎ (01492) 642031
Printed and published in Wales.

CONTENTS

Acknowledgements

I am grateful for the assistance received from the staff of Gwynedd Archives and County Library, Caernarfon; Thomas Roberts and the staff of the Archives and Library of the University of Wales, Bangor; National Library of Wales, Aberystwyth, and the Department of Botany, National Museum of Wales, Cardiff, and Serena K. Marner (Herbarium manager, Fielding-Druce Herbarium) of the Department of Plant Sciences, University of Oxford. I am indebted to Dr Iwan Edgar for his consultation and for permitting me the use of his Ph.D thesis on William Salesbury's Herbal, and to Dr Brynley F. Roberts and Gwynn Ellis for reading the original manuscript text and providing me with much valued opinions and encouragement. I would also like to thank those, who, during the course of conducting their own researches, brought to my attention certain facts relating to my chosen subject, namely, Wil Aaron, Dafydd Guto Ifan, the late Professor Bedwyr Lewis Jones, Edgar W. Parry, Medwen Roberts, D. Whiteside Thomas, and Reverend Dafydd Wyn Wiliam. I appreciate the kindness of Mr Owen George Hughes of Llanberis who granted me the use of his great-grandfather's pocket book for consultation and for permitting me to quote freely from its contents. My thanks are also due to Dr Fred Rumsey and Griff Williams for providing some of the photographs which appear in the book. I have for a considerable number of years, had the privilege of having among my correspondents and field companions Arthur Chater, William Condry, Robert Lewis and R.H. Roberts, whose advice, support and knowledge have been a constant inspiration. One debt which I can record but regretably can never repay is to the late Evan Roberts of Capel Curig, who was the foremost authority on the alpine plants of Snowdonia . . . *disgybl oeddwn, ti a'm dysgawdd* . . .

Dewi Jones, Pen-y-groes
February 1996.

FOREWORD

For over thirty years I have had an interest in the history of the botanical exploration of Wales. As a technician, and later student, in the Department of Botany, University College of Wales, Aberystwyth, in the early 1960s, I was fortunate enough to come into contact with the late Price W. Carter. Percy, as he was affectionately known, was the pre-eminent scholar on this subject, and published innumerable papers and articles, including the History of Botanical Exploration in most of the Welsh and many English counties. He presented me with a copy of his *Botanical Exploration in Cardiganshire*, and I was hooked! I found the whole topic quite enthralling and, as a very green and naive teenager, decided that this was a subject that I would like to pursue. Fate took a hand, when, after graduating, I was fortunate enough to be appointed Assistant Keeper of Botany at the National Museum of Wales. While browsing through its extensive library, I came across a little book containing a manuscript in the hand of the Reverend Hugh Davies. This consisted of a copy of *Doctor Richardson's directions for Welch Plants to Dr John Jac. Dillenius* dated May 7th, 1726 and running to 12 pages, and a transcript of Samuel Brewer's diary of his journey to North Wales with Dillenius in 1726 and his subsequent stay in Snowdonia. This prompted me to start thinking about preparing a book which would cover the history of botanical exploration of Wales and eventually a booklet, *Plant Hunting in Wales*, was published by the National Museum of Wales in 1973. Some years after the death of Mr Carter (in 1971), I was given his unpublished writings on the history of botanical exploration in Monmouthshire and Pembrokeshire and agreed to prepare these for publication. *Some account of the history of botanical exploration in Pembrokeshire* appeared in 1986 and the Monmouthshire paper is now ready for publication.

In this account of the botanists and guides of Snowdonia, Dewi Jones has produced a book that I have no doubt Percy Carter would have approved of. This is no mere passing glance at the personalities involved but an in-depth study which presents scholarly research in a style that makes the book difficult to put down. Whilst reading it I was constantly amazed at the amount of detail that is crammed in, but always so clearly presented that it never becomes overpowering, nor does it detract from the easy flow of the text.

We are led from the serene existence of William Salesbury in the middle of the 16th century, through the wretchedness of poverty and squalor in which many of the country folk existed in the 17th to 19th centuries, to the professional tourist's guides of the late 19th century. The story never flags, and out of this poverty, acts of courage by those who acted as guides stand out as beacons of light in a dark period. The contrast between the life style of the English gentry who wished to see the sights and plants of Snowdonia and the local peasantry who guided them, although never dwelt upon, is an underlying theme and the book thus gives us an insight into the conditions that existed during that period.

Dewi Jones is to be congratulated on writing a highly readable account of a fascinating subject. An achievement even more remarkable when one realises that he is a self-taught scholar and botanist who has never belonged to a botanical society! He describes his acquaintance with the late Evan Roberts of Capel Curig as a turning point in his hobby for it was Mr Roberts who introduced him to County Floras and the historical aspect of plant hunting. We too have much to thank Evan Roberts for. Dewi Jones has proved himself a meticulous researcher, an able and lucid author, and an accomplished field botanist. He is in his element among the wild cwms of Snowdonia climbing some difficult crag to see how the *Woodsia alpina* or some other plant is doing and does his 'rounds' of them annually.

It is surely no exaggeration to say that Dewi Jones has assumed the mantle of those botanists of old that he writes about so passionately and is without doubt today's leading authority on Snowdon's plants.

R. Gwynn Ellis, June 1995.

William Salesbury's Herbal

The first unpublished localized records of Welsh plants appear in a 16th century manuscript which was written by William Salesbury.

William Salesbury (c1520-1591) was perhaps the best example of the renaissance Polymath in Wales. Only a few details are known about his life, his major achievement being the translating of the New Testament from the original Greek into Welsh. He was born at Llansannan, Denbighshire, the second son of Ffwg ap Robert ap Salbri Hen, and Annes, daughter of Wiliam ap Gruffudd ap Robin of Cochwillan. We have his place of birth on his own authority from a passage written in the Herbal on page 6a which describes the habitat and locality of the marsh-mallow (*Althaea officinalis*) 'Mewn tir gwlyb phraeth tyf y rhyw hwnn o'r hockys a mi ai gwelais yn tyfy yn y ddol y dan Blas Meredydd ap Grono yn llan Sannan sef yn y plwy y ganwyt vi'. (This species grows on wet land and I have seen it growing in a meadow below the mansion of Meredydd ap Grono in Llansannan, namely the parish in which I was born).

He was a member of one of the junior branches of the powerful Salesbury family which was established at Llewenni in the vale of Clwyd before 1334, but spent the greater part of his life at Plas Isa, Llanrwst, and this qualifies him to be included among the botanists connected with Snowdonia.

During his term of education at Oxford, being resident at Broadgate Hall he added to his knowledge of Latin a proficiency in Greek and Hebrew, and it was

Plas Isa, Llanrwst, the home of William Salesbury

9

here also that he decided to leave the Roman Catholic Church and become an ardent Protestant.

He later married Catrin Llwyd, sister of Dr Elis Prys of Plas Iolyn, Ysbyty Ifan, who was known as 'y Doctor Coch', (the Red Doctor); moreover, William Salesbury's brother Robert married Lowri, who was also a sister of Elis Prys. Robert Salesbury died in 1540 at which time a quarrel arose between William Salesbury and Gwen and Elin, his late brother's daughters, concerning the inheritence of the family's lands and property. In order to resolve the dispute, the matter was put before a panel of arbitrators, among whom was Dr Elis Prys, the guardian and uncle of the two girls. The dispute was temporarily settled when the arbitrators published their judgement of the matter on 4 November 1546. The document records that William Salesbury 'put away' his wife Catrin Llwyd and that Elis Prys had implored him to take her back 'and her to kepe and use as his wiff'. It is not possible to explain what motives Salesbury had for behaving towards his wife in this manner as no more evidence has come to light concerning the matter. An incident, perhaps relating to these circumstances, happened (probably in January 1547) while Salesbury was on his way to London. He was riding between Wrexham and Holt when he was attacked by Elis Prys and a number of his companions, forced to dismount and robbed of a box containing documents and a wallet of money. Salesbury later sent a complaint regarding this, to the Star Chamber Court in London, but there remains no documented evidence as to how Elis Prys and his companions answered the charge.

Between the years 1547 and 1552 William Salesbury wrote seven books and one manuscript; *A Dictionary in Englyshe and Welshe* (1547) was aimed at assisting the Welsh people to learn the English language, therefore complying with and promoting the policies of Henry VIII. Further proof of these ideals appears in some of his other works; but his ideals however must not be misconstrued. His life's work bears testimony of an unwavering desire to see the Welsh language flourish. His two main motives were to make the Holy Scriptures available to the Welsh people in their native language, and also to develop and encourage learning and knowledge among them. These ambitions suffered a setback for a period during the reign of Queen Mary (1553-1558) when the Roman Catholic faith was revived, and Latin was once more ordained to be the language of worship.

Further changes followed the premature death of Mary and a law was passed during the early part of the reign of her successor Elizabeth I directing the translation of the Bible and the Book of Common Prayer into Welsh. Salesbury was invited to assist Richard Davies, the bishop of St Davids with the work and The New Testament and the Book of Common Prayer were completed and published by 1567.

William Salesbury wrote his Herbal sporadically between 1568 and 1578, and it was not completed (in its incomplete form) until after that time. The principal sources consulted by him for this work were the works of Leonard Fuchs *De Historia Stirpium* (1542) and William Turner's *A New Herbal &c* (1st part London 1551; 2nd part Cologne 1562; complete work in 3 parts London 1568). These authors are acknowledged frequently by Salesbury; Fuchs he considered as being the foremost botanist of the age while Turner was immortalized as being 'the Father of British Botany'. The two ancient classical writers which are most frequently mentioned in the work are Dioscorides and Galen; the former was a 1st century Greek physican, author of a major work which was considered as being the standard medical manual of the age. The book combined a description of the plants with details of their medicinal values, and provided the main source for the books of Fuchs and Turner. Galen lived in the second century of the Christian era and was for a time one of the prime physicians attending the imperial family at Rome. He is referred to by Salesbury as 'yr hen bennadur Galenus' which according to Stanton Roberts (p.xxvi) 'is not literally correct, but "pennadur" (sovereign) may have been used to imply he was a king among physicians, and his reputation among medical men for fourteen centuries after his death would justify such a compliment'.

The fact that Salesbury kept a record of the plants he observed in the different localities that he visited becomes apparent as one studies the manuscript. (N.L.W. Ms 4581). The marsh mallow (*Althaea officinalis*), already mentioned gives us the name of his place of birth, and another plant to be given a locality is the common restharrow (*Ononis repens*).

'Y Dagaratr. 15/ Anonis et Ononis yn Llatin . . E gephir gwelet y llyseun hwnn yn tyfy yn ampl gar llaw llwybyr a dywys ar hyt y meysydd ir plas yn Lleweni. /' [29b] (This plant grows amply close to the path which leads across the fields to the mansion at Llewenni.) [Denbighshire].

On page 67b the maidenhair spleenwort (*Asplenium trichomanes*) is noted as growing 'Ar y bont vaen ar Lugwy y gwelais i lawer yn tyfy'. (On the stone bridge over the Llugwy I saw many growing).

Among the fine fronds of hart's tongue (*Phyllitis scolopendrium*) he found at Llannefydd were specimens which measured up to eighteen inches and as broad as the breadth of ones hand, he claims. He also describes several forked varieties of this fern, and others divided into three or four parts.

'Tafod yr Hydd. 51./ Y rhei teccaf ac amplaf ac a welais i etto sy yn tyfy o bop tu y bwll y vwyall mewn glyn coedioc or eiddo Tudur ap Robert or tu dwyrain a Robert Wynn ap Ieuan ap dd or tu gorllewin./ Mi a gefais yno rei o'r dail hyd o hanner llath o vewn lled llaw rhei a ei blaenau yn phorchoc a rhei yn dri phwrch sef yn gohany yn bedwar blaen val osclae corn ben garw./ Yn emyl Talacrae y tyf rhei tec iawn'. ([69b] The finest I ever saw grew either side of 'bwll y vwyall' in a wooded glen on land belonging to Tudur ap Robert on the eastern side of

Robert Wyn ap Ieuan ap Dafydd from the west. There I gathered fronds up to half a yard within the breadth of a hand some with forked ends and some thrice forked and others forked into four ends similar to a stag's horn. There grow some very fine ones near Talacre.)

These are the observations of a botanist reflected three hundred years later by the 'variety hunters' of the Victorian age. William Salesbury, unlike the herbalists of his time who studied plants purely for medical reasons, did so in order to learn more about them.

In his note on garlic (*Allium sativum*) Salesbury discloses that he spent some part of his childhood in Lancashire; it is thought by some that he may have attended a school there to learn English.

'Ac yd y daw im cof a mi yn vachgen yn swydd [157b] Lancastr myfy a welais yr ail rhyw yn tyfy yn y garddae . . . a garllec Mair y galwent./' ([157a-157b] As far as I can recall when I was a boy in Lancashire I saw the second species growing in gardens . . . they called it the garlic of Mary).

The claim made by Fuchs that the mistletoe (*Viscum album*) is to be found growing on oak is repudiated by Salesbury on page 73a.

'Byth ni thyf yr vchelfa ar y ddayar anid ymbric yspaddat, efyll nei ellyc prenn as ys y dywaid Phwcsius yn enwedic ar y Dderwen yr hyn ni welais i etto, nac yn tyfy ar vn pren y tu yma i Lan Gollen./ Y cynayaf y clescir ef ai rawn arno eithyr mi welais vis Mowrth yn emyl y bont ar Geirioc vn llwyn or vchelfa ar cibae gwynion hynny arnaw./' ([173a] The mistletoe never grows on the ground but in hawthorn, apple and pear tree branches and allthough Fuchs states that it grows on oak I have never seen it as yet, nor have I seen it growing on any tree this side of Llangollen . . . The earliest I have observed it with berries was in March near Pont ar Geiriog (near Chirk) having one bush with white berries, but from thence to Ludlow I found none with berries).

Of the chamomile (*Anthemis*) he writes that it is found growing frequently in the British Isles outside the boundaries of gardens.

' . . . O bleit mi welais ar Grin Lleweni lanerchae llydain o hono [10b] eb ddim cymysc llysae er eill nac vn glaswelltyn ynto./ Mi welais hefyd lwyni o hono yn tyfy ar y gwyllt parth gogledd y plas Tudur ap Robert yn Llan Yvyth./' ([10a-10b] I have observed this on the green at Llewenni growing in broad patches with no other plant or grass growing amongst it. I have also seen bushes of it growing on the wild land which lies to the north of the mansion of Tudur ap Robert Wyn in Llannefydd).

There are some annotations on the margins of this page made by a more recent hand which state. 'felly mae ar y marian yn Nolgellau' and 'ac ár heol y fedw yn llansantffraid glyn dawrdwy' (it grows similarly on the 'marian' at Dolgellau) and (on the birch road at Llansantffraid Glyn Dyfrdwy).

Common gromwell (*Lithospermum officinale*) was observed by Salesbury growing on the slope between the town walls of Denbigh and the houses of

Hugh Dryhurst and Robert Huxley. He also records the plant from either side of a stream at Whitford in Flintshire.

'Had y Gromandi . . . Lithospermon. Gnawd ir llysae hyn dyfy mewn mannae geirwon vchel. Ac wrth hynny chwi a gewch ei gwelet wy yn tyfy ar y lledfron rhwng gwal tref Dinbech ar tai nid amgen na'r tu disathr y Duy Huw Dryhwrst a thuy Robert Hwxley. Ac etto mi welais lwyn tec or llysae hyn ar y gwastat o boptu i ryd Wtphord ar Ddyfrdwy. Ac wy a dyfant o hehir wy mewn garddae.' (105a).

The family home of Llewenni is mentioned again in the paragraph dealing with the burnet-saxifrage (*Pimpinella saxifraga*). Salesbury records it growing in clumps in a field which was crossed as one walked from the town of Denbigh to the mansion at Llewenni.

'Tormaen./92./ . . . Oenanthe yn Groec a Llatin a Philipendula yn y Llatin. Y mae y llyseun hwn yn tyfy mewn tumpathe gan y cae phordd yr eloch ar draet o Dinbech ir plas yn Lleweni./ (117b).

'Surianbren', a suitably descriptive Welsh name for the wild cherry (*Prunus avium*), is stated as growing on the left hand side of the road leading from Llanbedr Dyffryn Clwyd towards the mountain.

'Edrychwch goruwch eich penn ar y llaw asswy pan eloch ar hyd y geuphordd sy yn tywys o Lanbedr yn Dyffryn Clwyd y tu ar mynydd a chwi a gewch weled prenne sirian cochion yn tyfy ehunain o braphter anyscedol.' (91b)

An account of the tragic death of a young boy from Hawarden follows the descriptive note of the deadly nightshade (*Atropa belladonna*) which he calls by the Welsh name (borrowed from the Latin) 'Y Morela'. (118 151a-151b). Salesbury states that he was informed of this by John Edward of Chirk who spoke of two boys from Hawarden who passed into a coma after eating the fruit of this plant. One of the boys came from a poor family who at the time had suffered several deaths resulting from the plague, and on believing that the boy had suffered a similar fate promptly interred him. The other boy in the meantime regained consciousness and revealed to his family that he and his friend had been eating the fruit of the deadly nightshade prior to the time they became ill. Another person, namely Elisa ap Wiliam of Penllyn is named as having told Salesbury that the incident happened at Caergwrle.

Salesbury also notes the bulrush (*Typha*) growing in the moat of Whittington Castle, near Oswestry. 'Yr Hesc Melfedoc 138/ Mewn corsydd a llynnae y tyf. Mi a welais o hono yn y llyn sydd yn cylchyny castell y Drewen yn gyfagos i dref Groes Oswallt./' (173b).

He transplanted a plant of wild radish (*Raphanus raphanistrum*) from a meadow on the western side of the Abbey at Maenan, to his garden at Plas Isa and adds that the plant was frequently seen growing 'wild', naming one such locality near Geufron, Llandwrog south of Caernarfon. Salesbury also states having seen this plant growing in the gardens of Phowk ap Rhys in Denbigh, and Rhys ap Dafydd ap Ieuan in Llannefydd.

'Y Reddic. 112 . . . gweirglodd y menych gynt y tu gorllewin y Vonachloc Aberconwy sef yr hwn a vuriwyd i lawr yn emyl Aberllechoc ac o yno y perais ei ysmuto im gardd./ Digon ampl y metrir arnun yn tyfy yn wyllt eithyr mi ai gwelais wy yn tyfy eb ei planny mewn llwyn dyrys lle gelwir y Geufron yn plwyf Llan Twroc yn Arvon./ Mi ai gwelais wy hefyd yn tyfy yn gardd Phowk ap Rhys of yn Dinbych ac yn gardd Rhys ap dd ap Ieuan yn Llanyvydd [--] (140a).

Obviously in Salesbury's time botany as we know it was in its infancy. Nevertheless it is noteworthy that Salesbury could be designated as a first true Welsh botanist and that his Herbal could be arguably considered to be the first Welsh modern scientific book. He is remarkable in the fact that he precedes all others in having an interest in plants for their own sake and is at times ready to question the validity of claims made by even the foremost herbal writers of the day.

Just as interesting as the story of Salesbury's life and botanical researches is the way in which the text of his Herbal has reached us. The original manuscript is lost, but three copies of the work are known to have survived. One of these transcripts came into the possession of the Reverend John Peter of Bala (Ioan Pedr 1833-1877) in 1868, as an inscription on the title page implies, and it was he who gave it the title of *Llysieulyfr Meddyginiaethol gan William Salesbury* (Medicinal Herbal by William Salesbury). An earlier note in the manuscript shows that it was copied in 1763. Following the death of the Reverend John Peter the manuscript was bought by Principal Thomas Charles Edwards who later gave it to the Welsh Library of the University College of Wales, Aberystwyth from where it was passed on to the National Library of Wales in 1905. It was from this version of the manuscript (N.L.W Ms 686) that Evan Stanton Roberts edited and published his *Llysieulyfr Meddyginiaethol* (1916).

Another transcript of Salesbury's original manuscript was discovered by Sir John Williams (1840-1926, principal founder of the National Library of Wales) earlier this century at the Old Hall, Cowbridge and this was presented to the National Library of Wales in 1922 by its owners Miss Edmondes and Mrs Laurence Williams, Bonvilston Cottage, Bonvilston. This manuscript (N.L.W. Ms 4581) is in the hand of Roger Morris (fl. 1590) of Coed y Talwrn, Llanfair Dyffryn Clwyd and the following inscription appears on page 187a. (Page 206 on N.L.W. Ms 686).

'Hyd yma o lyfr o law W. Salsburie/a gawsid ei venthic gan Syr Tomas ap Wiliam/1597/Deo gratias.' (Up to this part in the hand of W. Salsburie borrowed from Sir Tomas ap Wiliam 1597).

According to the above testimony the manuscript up to page 187a was a transcript copied by Roger Morris from the original work of William Salesbury, then in the possession of Sir Tomos ap Wiliam. This was Thomas

Wiliems (1545 or 46-1622?) of Trefriw, the learned lexicographer, physician, scribe and priest, who by his own testimony was born at 'Ardhe'r Menych dan droet mynydh yr yri'. This place, Arddu'r Mynaich, stands a short distance to the north of Trefriw. Unlike his contemporary William Salesbury who was a Protestant Thomas Wiliems was a Catholic, but Thomas Wiliems will be remembered chiefly for compiling a Latin-Welsh dictionary which was never published but was used extensively by Dr John Davies of Mallwyd (c.1567-1644) as the basis for his *Antiquae Linguae Britannicae Dictionarum Duplex* (1632), in which is included a *Botanologium* much used by later botanists.

The manuscripts of Roger Morris were dispersed soon after his death (circa 1603) and some of them came into the possession of Thomas Evans of Hendreforfudd, Edeyrnion, near Corwen; among these it is believed, was the original manuscript Herbal of William Salesbury. From this period on, the fate of the original work remains unknown, but there is evidence to suggest that either the original or the transcript (N.L.W. Ms 4581) came to be acquired by Robert Davyes of Gwysanau, Flintshire sometime before 1633. This is based upon the fact that the list of Welsh plant names published in Thomas Johnson's revised edition of Gerard's *Herbal* (1633) was submitted by 'Robert Davyes of Guissaney'. This list is said to contain plant names which could only have come from William Salesbury's Herbal. Nothing further is known of transcript N.L.W. Ms 4581 until the mid 18th century by which time three of its previous owners had written their names on it. They are Edward Evans (page 1a) Evan Thomas (page 95b) who adds a note stating he acquired it from Ellis Edwards in 1763, and Thomas Evans (page 119b). The Evan Thomas whose name appears on page 95b was Evan Thomas (d.1781) of Cwmhwylfod, Sarnau near Bala, a notable transcriber and owner of manuscripts. He transcribed another copy (i.e. N.L.W. Ms 686) from the earlier one in the hand of Roger Morris (N.L.W. Ms 4581) and this formed the basis from which E. Stanton Roberts, as mentioned earlier, edited and published under the title *Llysieulyfr Meddyginiaethol &c* (1916).

Another copy, albeit an incomplete one, of the original work is kept at the Cardiff Central Library (Ms 2.973). The name of Thomas Wiliems of Trefriw is frequently referred to on various pages of this manuscript; it was he who loaned Roger Morris the original work so therefore it is possible that Cardiff Ms 2.973 is the remnant of yet another copy of Salesbury's work.

Roger Morris' transcript (N.L.W. Ms 4581) has survived almost intact and consists of 400 pages numbered up to 200b, of which 198a and 199b are missing. An index for the plant names has been appended to the main text; these pages have not been numbered.

Thomas Glynne, Glynllifon and his Friends

On the morning of 3 August, 1639 a party of botanists rode out of Glynllifon near Caernarfon and headed in the direction of Snowdon. The leader was Thomas Johnson, an apothecary from London, a man who had already published a number of pamphlets giving details of his botanical discoveries from other parts of the kingdom, but this journey differed from the previous plant hunting expeditions which he had undertaken in that neither of his companions seem to have been an apothecary. Johnson (c.1597-1644) was a native of Selby, Yorkshire, and served his apprenticeship as an apothecary from 1620 until 1628 under William Bell at Westminster in the parish of St Margarets; by 1639 he had a business on Snow Hill, in the City of London. He published an account of his journey through North Wales in a book entitled *Mercurii Botanici Pars Altera* in 1641. A portion of the original Latin work was translated into English by W. Jenkyn Thomas and published in a booklet entitled *The Itinerary of a Botanist* in Bangor in 1908. The foreword of the translated work was written by Lewis Davies Jones (Llew Tegid) a prominent literary figure.

Thomas Glynne of Glynllifon, squire and county M.P., was himself a

Glynllifon, prior to it being destroyed by fire in 1836.
The original house, where Johnson stayed in 1639, stands
on the left hand side, behind the 18th century mansion.

botanist, had been corresponding with Johnson during the early 1630s, and had been sending him a number of plant specimens and details of localities which were published by Johnson in his revised edition of Gerard's *Herbal* in 1633. These are the first localised records published of native Welsh plants being collected and recorded by a Welshman. Johnson states that 'The red floured Mountaine Avens [*Geum rivale*] was found growing in Wales by my much honoured friend Mr Thomas Glynne who sent me some plants thereof to our Herbarists, in whose gardens it thriveth exceedingly.' Thomas Glynne was the first in Britain to record the discovery of the cottonweed (*Otanthus maritimus*). 'I also had it sent me,' said Johnson, 'from my worshipfull friend Mr Thomas Glynne who gathered it upon the sea coast of Wales.' It would appear from the writings of Johnson that the cottonweed used to grow on the coast near Dinas Dinlle during those days, which is only a mile and a half from Glynllifon. The translation states: ' . . . we went to the sea shore, which is not further than a mile from the house, and there we dug up the *Soldanella* [sea bindweed (*Calystegia soldanella*)] and the *Gnaphalium marinum*. [cottonweed (*Otanthus maritimus*)]. The *Roman* soldiers had a station here, on the very edge of the sea, the remains of which are still to be clearly seen.' The 'remains' to which Johnson refers were probably those of the hill fort at Dinas Dinlle.

Johnson came to North Wales via Chester, Flint and Holywell, stayed one night at Rhuddlan before going on to Aberconwy where they were met by one of Thomas Glynne's servants, who led them to Bodysgallen Hall, the home of Robert Wynne, where Thomas Glynne was waiting for them. The following day they continued their journey by crossing Penmaenmawr and passing through Bangor and Caernarfon before arriving at Glynllifon on 1 August after a journey that had taken 12 days to complete.

One of Johnson's companions during this visit was Edward Morgan, described by Johnson as a student of botany who had been brought along as interpreter. Little is known of Morgan's early years, but it is believed that he was born in North Wales about 1619, and later moved to London as a young man to study plants. Later in life Morgan was certainly held in high esteem by the leading botanists of the day, and Brynley F. Roberts in his published lecture *Edward Lhuyd the making of a Scientist* (1980) mentions the close relationship that existed between Morgan and Edward Lhuyd and asks. 'Was Lhuyd one of Morgan's pupils?' Morgan was later to become superintendent at the Westminster Physic Garden which appears to have been established by Dr William Howe about 1655, and refers to himself as 'Herbalist to the Physick Garden in Westminster'. John Evelyn the diarist visited Morgan in 1658 and wrote, 'I went to see the Medical Garden at Westminster, well stored with plants under Morgan, a very skilful botanist.' Morgan was also well known to John Ray the naturalist, who presented him with a copy of his *Cambridge Catalogue* following a visit he made to the Garden to collect seeds and plants for the gardens of Trinity College, Cambridge. William Howe published his *Phytologia Britannica* in 1650 and in his personal copy the author has annotated a list of plants, together with their localities, which had been discovered by Morgan. The list proves that he was a knowledgeable botanist and a diligent plant collector. Howe had also a copy of one of Thomas Johnson's other works *Descriptio in Agrum Cantianum* and in this he had noted the following, 'consult Morgan about Orchis'. In William Coles' book *The Art of Simpling* (1656) William Howe is described as 'one of the Masters of the Westminster Physic Garden', and Edward Morgan as 'gardiner'.

The beginning of August is not an ideal time to look for alpine plants in Snowdonia; the visit should have been made two months earlier. Despite the lateness of the season they managed to collect in a single day, a considerable number of the choice plants for which Snowdon is famous. It has long been debated whether or not Johnson did in fact ascend Snowdon. In his book he notes the '*stygiae etiam hinc & inde paludes, quarum maxima Daemonis domilicum ab incolus vocatur*' and this might well refer to the Devil's Kitchen (Twll Du) in the Cwm Idwal area. In view of the local help he received, it seems likely that it was Snowdon that he visited, and the list of plants which he records for the day suggests this also. The first plant listed is the northern rock-cress (*Arabis petraea*) and Clogwyn Du'r Arddu has always been a stronghold for this alpine flower; very little of it grows anywhere else in Snowdonia. Also recorded are mountain sorrel (*Oxyria digyna*) roseroot (*Sedum rosea*) moss campion (*Silene acaulis*) alpine saxifrage (*Saxifraga nivalis*) starry saxifrage (*Saxifraga stellaris*) alpine saw-wort (*Saussurea alpina*) and dwarf willow (*Salix herbacea*), as well as to Johnson's surprise, such maritime plants as thrift (*Armeria maritima*), and sea rush (*Juncus maritimus*), or sharp rush (*Juncus acutus*).

Despite the fact that Johnson had a local man for companion, nevertheless during this visit the party decided to hire the services of a hill farmer's boy to guide them to Snowdon. This is the first written record of a guide being hired in Snowdonia, and the success of the venture must surely be attributed partly, if not wholly, to the guide who led them to the habitats of the rare plants.

These early mountaineers were ordinary hill farmers whose forefathers had tended their flocks, dug for peat and hunted on the same wild mountain terrain for generations. History and folklore had been passed down among them from father to son in the customary fashion and with it, in some instances came the specialised knowledge needed to prepare herbal medicine. It would therefore have been essential for certain members of these isolated communities to know the habitats of the plants used for medicinal purposes. The mountain plants were believed to contain healing qualities similar to, if not stronger than those of the lowland species, and localities such as Clogwyn Du'r Arddu, Clogwyn y Garnedd, Cwmglas Mawr and Cwmglas Bach on Snowdon, and Cwm Idwal and the cliffs around the Devil's Kitchen on the Glyder were noted for their

Clogwyn Du'r Arddu (Photo: Griff Williams)

variety of flowers from the earliest times. It must also be remembered that these early herbalists and apothecaries could identify plants from foliage alone, a necessary skill during out of season botanical excursions.

Later that day, having reached the summit, the party halted, and to quote the translation of Johnson's words, 'sat down in the midst of the clouds, and first of all we arranged in order the plants we had at our peril collected among the rocks and precipices, and then we ate the food we had brought with us.' One can easily imagine a group of dark cloaked gentlemen, sheltering among the summit rocks of Snowdon, reflecting on the day's events and eating out of their baskets, where they also carried their plant specimens.

The party returned to Glynllifon after the Snowdon excursion and on the following day Thomas Glynne led them over to Anglesey. Travellers from the southern part of Caernarfonshire wishing to cross the Menai Straits to Anglesey in those days did so from Abermenai, and they visited Llanddwyn Island and Newborough recording such plants as rock sea-lavender (*Limonium binervosum*) and the sea spleenwort (*Asplenium marinum*). Johnson also notes how the local people of Newborough wove mats and made ropes from marram (*Ammophila arenaria*). This local industry continued until the 1930s. An invitation from Richard Bulkeley of Baron Hill brought Johnson and his party to Beaumaris, at the eastern corner of the island, and here they were informed 'that there was no spot in all that country where rarer or more plants grew than on the high mountain, not more than four miles from Bangor'. The site referred to was, most probably, the Ysgolion Duon cliffs between Carnedd Dafydd and Carnedd Llywelyn; a locality which is still favoured by field botanists today. It is an interesting fact that the site was known to the inhabitants of Beaumaris as long ago as the seventeenth century. A guide was hired at Llanllechid, and it is often repeated as to how this local mountaineer failed to live up to the standards set by his Snowdon counterpart. Johnson records, 'after we had come to the ridge of the mountain we were taken round it by the guide, enveloped in dense wet clouds, but we failed to persuade him to take us to the precipices, where alone the rarer plants grew . . . Our rustic guide feared the Eagles nesting there, for they are accustomed to swoop crosswise on swift pinion before the faces of the cattle feeding on the precipices, and by suddenly frightening them, make them fall down the rocks and become their prey.'

The disillusioned party then decided to abandon their quest, in view of the adverse weather conditions and the conduct of their guide, and returned to Bangor for the night before returning to Glynllifon the following day. Two days later Johnson's party left North Wales and returned to London via Machynlleth, Ludlow, Gloucester and Oxford. A year after publishing his *Mercurii Botanici* war broke out between Charles I and the Parliamentary forces under Oliver Cromwell. Johnson joined the King's Army and was promoted to the rank of Lieutenant Colonel, but was wounded during an engagement near Basing House, Hampshire in 1644 and he died soon after.

We are indebted to Thomas Johnson, not only for the account he wrote of his early botanical tour of North Wales, but also for giving us the names of two of the earliest Welsh botanists Thomas Glynne of Glynllifon and Edward Morgan of the Westminster Physic Garden.

According to Glyn Roberts, writing on the Glynne and Wynne families of Glynllifon in the Transactions of the Caernarvonshire Historical Society (1948) Thomas Glynne 'was a man of no outstanding qualities' and he makes no mention of his botanical interests. He was elected M.P. for Caernarfonshire in 1624 and again to the 'Short Parliament' of 1640. He was Constable of Caernarfon Castle from 1646 until his death in 1648 and supported the Parliament, but before 1646 he served as a 'Commissioner of Array' and was a Colonel in the King's Army. The late W. Gilbert Williams of Rhostryfan, a highly respected local historian, mentions briefly in his book *Arfon y Dyddiau Gynt* that Thomas Glynne was a noted botanist and that a plant had been named after him, but no proof to substantiate this claim has as yet been found, as none of his botanical papers seem to have survived.

Edward Morgan left the Garden and Westminster about 1678 and was succeeded as Gardener there by a Mr Rusholm who held the post until the end

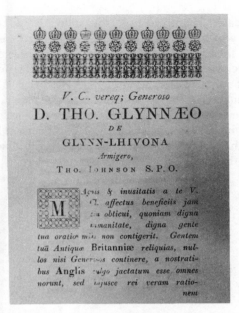

Thomas Johnson's tribute to Thomas Glynne in the Mercurii Botanici

of 1687 when the garden was closed and the plants dispersed.

By 1680 Morgan had returned to Wales and was living at Bodysgallen near Llandudno, the seat of Robert Wynne, whom he had visited with Thomas Johnson during the botanical excursion to North Wales in 1639. During this period it appears that he was also being employed at Llanforda near Oswestry, at the home of Edward Lloyd, father of the famous Welsh naturalist Edward Lhuyd. While working at Llanforda he introduced Lloyd to a seedsman called Fuller, and Lloyd in return acted for Morgan during a legal transaction which permitted him to retain his interest in the plants in the Physic Garden at Westminster. Brynley F. Roberts, in his paper on Edward Lhuyd mentioned earlier, notes the fact that Morgan, who had taken pupils earlier at Westminster, also had some under him at Llanforda. A letter to Dr Morison dated 3 December, 1680 refers to 'two pupils yt have last year taken a gt deal of pains in Briddin hills, snowden fforest, severall mountains rocks Cliffs by ye sea side, sea shore in many places, wee searched for ye solidago sarasenica but wee were ill directed.'

There can be no doubt that Edward Lhuyd held Morgan in high esteem, a respect that could have nurtured by an earlier teacher and pupil relationship. Lhuyd, in a letter to David Lloyd in 1695 compliments Morgan by saying that he was 'one that, in his way has deserved as well as any in England; a man equally commendable for his good life, and indefatigable industry'.

Morgan could well have been the teacher of Edward Lhuyd, as Roberts' paper points out, for Lhuyd had listed plants and localities in one of his note books which match those mentioned by Morgan in his letter of 3 December 1680 ' . . . Snowdon hils, Breiddin hil . . . ' etc.

Edward Morgan died in 1689, and his collection of plants, 2,000 in number went to the Ashmolean Museum, Oxford and are now kept at the Bodleian Library, Oxford. He also possessed a fine study of books, which according to Lhuyd was 'worth abt 10li wch he has told me several times he would leave me': The fate of this library remains unknown.

John Ray and Edward Lhuyd

John Ray (1627-1705), the most celebrated of English naturalists, journeyed through North Wales in 1658 and 1662. He was born the son of a village blacksmith at Black Notley, near Braintree, Essex, on 29 November 1627. It was during his time at Braintree School that his outstanding qualities and exceptional talents were first noticed by the master, a Mr Love, and also by Samuel Collins, the Vicar of Braintree who encouraged further education. Ray went up to Catharine Hall, Cambridge on 28 June 1644 following his admittance on 12 May; ironically in the same year that the first of the botanical travellers into Wales died, the London apothecary Thomas Johnson.

He was ordained in London in 1660, but his strong beliefs led to his refusing to accept Charles II Act of Uniformity, and thus he resigned his office at Cambridge in 1662.

John Ray began to take an interest in plants while recovering from a bout of illness he suffered at Cambridge. He was no physician and studied plants

John Ray (1627-1705)

merely so that he could learn more about them, unlike the herbalists and apothecaries of the same period who studied plants for medical reasons. During the years that spanned the lifetimes of Thomas Johnson and John Ray, botany began to emerge as a seperate subject. Cambridge in the 1650s was slowly recovering after the upheaval and disorder following the Civil War. This was the time which saw an increase in the studying of Science, and this clashed with the classical traditions of the Universities. Up until this time botany had received no official recognition as a subject, and when Ray and others went out to the countryside to study plants, they were ridiculed by their fellow students and others who supported the 'traditionalists'. Despite this he continued pursuing his chosen subject, and in 1660 he published a list of the plants he and his friends had recorded in the vicinity of Cambridge under the title *Catalogus Cantabrigiam*. It was the first published flora, albeit in Latin, of an English county. The first flora of a Welsh county did not appear until 1813, when the Reverend Hugh Davies published his catalogue for the plants of Anglesey entitled *Welsh Botanology*.

In 1658 John Ray entered North Wales by way of Chester, Holywell, St Asaph, Conwy and Bangor. This is what he notes from his first visit to Snowdonia.

'September the 1st, I left Carnarvon, intending for Snowden, having, for that Purpose, hired a Guide to conduct me to the Top of the Hill. But it rained so bad, that I was forced, within a Mile of the Town, to take shelter in a small Cottage. After that I proceeded to the foot of the Hill, where my Guide desponding, and being somewhat late, I was forced to dismiss him. This Night I lodged at Bethkellert.'

'September the 2nd. At Bethkellert I hired another Guide to the top of Snowden, we marched up on Foot about Four Miles. The top of the Mountain was covered with Clouds, so that I lost the Prospect usually taken from thence of the adjacent Country. Divers rare Plants I found on the Top and Sides of the Hill, which were then Strangers to me, *de quibus consule Catalogum*'.

It is interesting to note that during John Ray's time, guides to Snowdon could be hired at Caernarfon, and it is equally important that his is the first record of a Beddgelert mountain guide being hired. Ray on his return journey home through Bala and Shrewsbury heard about the death of Oliver Cromwell.

John Ray returned to North Wales in 1662, this time in the company of two other botanists Francis Willughby (1635-1672) and Phillip Skippon (fl. 1640-1674). They entered North Wales again through Chester, but this time they arrived in the heartland of Eryri by a route which took them through the mountains via Wrexham, Mold, Denbigh and Betws-y-coed, arriving at Bangor on 19 May. On this second visit Ray had come to Snowdonia at a better time of the year to see the mountain plants at their best. He made his first trip during September at which time the ferns and mosses are at their best, but most of the flowering plants are well and truly over. On the day following their arrival at Bangor, the party visited Carnedd Llywelyn, but had no better luck than Johnson did 23 years before. They also crossed over to Anglesey, visited Puffin Island and then rode across the island to Abermenai, where they found cottonweed (*Otanthus maritimus*) and sea stock (*Matthiola sinuata*) on the sea shore near the Ferry. They spent Sunday at Caernarfon after crossing the Menai Straits back to the mainland. On 26 May they went to Llanberis and on to Beddgelert recording Welsh poppy (*Meconopsis cambrica*) by the wayside and the small-white orchid (*Pseudorchis albida*) near Dolbadarn Castle: an orchid hitherto unknown to science. This plant is very rare and there have been no recent records of it from Snowdonia. On the following day the party ascended Snowdon, although it is not clear whether or not they gained the summit. They probably went up from Beddgelert, and recorded parsley fern (*Cryptogramma crispa*) mossy saxifrage (*Saxifraga hypnoides*) and roseroot (*Sedum rosea*) and four of the club-mosses. (There is no mention of a guide being with them during this visit.)

After the Snowdon visit the party left Snowdonia and visited Bardsey Island before going on to Harlech, of which Ray records. 'This is a miserable poor town, yet is governed by a mayor, two bailiffs and a recorder.' From Harlech the party moved southward to Aberdyfi, and Ray records mountain everlasting (*Antennaria dioica*) from 'the top of Plimllimon-hill', which they must have climbed on their way to Cardigan. They then continued their journey to Pembroke and crossed the southern part of Wales to Cydweli and Caerwent before leaving for Gloucester on 14 June.

The list of plants which Ray recorded from his two excursions into Snowdonia are listed in the following works. *Cataloguus Plantarum Angliae* (1670), *Fasciculus Stirpium Britannicarum* (1688) and the book which was for generations of botanists the most consulted work on British plants, the *Synopsis Methodica Stirpium Britannicarum*, which was first published in 1690, with a second edition in 1696, and a third in 1724.

It is not known if John Ray and Edward Lhuyd ever met, but they began corresponding during the summer of 1689, and it is clear that Lhuyd thought highly of England's foremost scientist ' . . . he is a man of the most agreeable temper imaginable, Mr Ray is doubtless the best acquainted with Natural History of any now living.'

Edward Lhuyd rose to be one of the most eminent Welshmen of his time and in 1706 Hans Sloane, who later became President of the Royal Society, described him as 'the best naturalist now in Europe.'

Lhuyd was the son of Edward Lloyd, Llanforda, near Oswestry, (whom we have already discussed) and Bridget Pryse, the daughter of Thomas Pryse, Glanfred near Aberystwyth. Being an illegitimate child there is a tradition that Lhuyd was born in Cardiganshire, but his actual birthplace according to

Edward Lhuyd (1660-1709)

records appears to be 'Loppington Parish' and most of his early life was spent in the Welsh part of Shropshire, near Oswestry.

He entered Jesus College, Oxford in October 1682, to study law, but even at this early stage in his career it became increasingly evident that his true interests lay in other matters. His name gradually came to be connected more with the Ashmolean Museum than with Jesus College, and following his matriculation he was appointed assistant to the Keeper, Dr Plot. When the post of Keeper became vacant in 1691 following Plot's retirement, Lhuyd succeeded him, and remained Keeper of the Ashmolean until his death in 1709.

Between the years 1691 and 1695 he was engaged in arranging and cataloguing his collection of British fossils and preparing notes on the Welsh counties for the publishers of the new edition of Camden's *Britannia*. He travelled the Celtic countries between 1695 and 1701, and from 1702 until 1707 he remained in Oxford writing his *Archeologia Britannica*, the first part of which was then published, *Glossography*. From 1707 until the time of his death he busied himself with arranging his notes and worked on historical matters. He did not live to complete his great work and died in June 1709, being buried in St Michael's Church, Oxford.

Lhuyd had begun to visit Snowdonia around 1680, and during the summer of 1688 he discovered over 40 new plants; this list was published by John Ray in his book *Synopsis Methodica Stirpium Britannicarum* (1690). Ray described the discoveries as the 'greatest ornament' to his book. The most important discovery, and the one which will always be associated with the name of Edward Lhuyd, did not appear in print until the second edition of the *Synopsis* was published in 1696. On the high cliffs above Cwm Idwal, on a site that was known as 'Trigyfylchau Rocks' in those days, Lhuyd discovered the small white lily which was firstly named *Bulbosa juncifolia &c.*, and then changed by Linnaeus to *Anthericum serotinum*. It was later realised that it was sufficiently distinct from other species of *Anthericum* to merit the formation of a new genus. The decision was taken to honour the finder and the plant is known today as *Lloydia serotina* (Snowdon lily). His extraordinary powers of observation become evident if one considers that when he first found the Snowdon lily it was not in flower. He saw only the leaves, and these could easily be taken for a clump of *Festuca* grass, a mistake that even the most experienced botanist could make. Lhuyd approached problems in a rational manner, and solved them systematically. For instance, earlier travellers wrote of the snows that covered Snowdon throughout the year, but Lhuyd, with his personal observations, and with the help of the local inhabitants soon proved them wrong. 'Generally speaking, there's no snow here from the end of April to the midst of September . . . It often snows on the tops of these mountains in May and June, but such snow, or rather sleet, melts as fast as it falls'. In 1696 he prepared questionaires which were distributed to various Parishes in Wales there to be completed by an eminent local resident.

Cwm Idwal
(Photo: Griff Williams)

27

The Vicar of Llanberis during this period was Thomas Evans, and on receiving one of the 'Parochial Queries' of Edward Lhuyd set about writing a report on the weather of the Llanberis district during the years 1697-98. The original manuscript is now kept at the National Library of Wales, Aberystwyth. The Reverend Evans was but one of the many who, around Wales, compiled the data for Lhuyd's 'Parochial Queries'.

The Church at Nant Peris

Thomas Evans was also a botanist, and he had provided visiting botanists with accommodation during their visits to the wilds of Snowdonia. Dr Richard Richardson (1663-1741) of North Brierley, Yorkshire, was a highly accomplished botanist and had the finest collection of British and foreign plants in the north of England, being the first to record the finding of the rare Killarney fern (*Trichomanes speciosum*) in England. He accompanied Edward Lhuyd during some of his trips to the Glyder mountain, and the Reverend Thomas Evans probably went along by virtue of his local knowledge. Another local man, William Griffith, acted as guide to Richardson during visits made to the Devil's Kitchen area on Glyder, and it was also noted that Lhuyd had shown the site of the Snowdon lily (*Lloydia serotina*) to Richardson at this time.

Edward Lhuyd also benefited from the local knowledge of William Rowlands, another native of Snowdonia, who collaborated with Lhuyd in similar work in 1693. Rowlands wrote several letters to Lhuyd in 1694 from Hafod y Llan near Beddgelert with directions that all communications be sent

Richard Richardson (1663-1741)

Snowdon lily (Lloydia serotina) from a woodcut in Ray's Synopsis (1724)

to 'W.R. near Beddgelert to be left with Mr Hugh Jones in Caernarfon, or at his house in Caernarfon'. William Rowlands' letters deals in an authoratative manner on subjects ranging from mountain plants to fossil shells and suggests a close relationship with Lhuyd. When Lhuyd held the post of keeper of the Ashmolean Museum, Rowlands had aspired to be his protégé and Lhuyd had hoped that this promising young man would accompany him during his forthcoming tour of the Celtic countries in 1697. The notes Rowlands compiled were used extensively by Lhuyd. They were published in the revised edition of *Britannia* which appeared in 1695 and which includes the etymology of place-names, age of the inhabitants, their illnesses and causes of death, ancient stone monuments and different branches of natural history. Rowlands' communications concerning the weather of Snowdonia agree with those of Thomas Evans, which dispel once and for all the old belief that snow lay on the mountains throughout the year. Equally interesting and conclusive are his revelations regarding eagles on Snowdon in the context of the Welsh name for eagle, *eryr*, and *Eryri*, Snowdonia, the abode of eagles. Rowlands does not state that he had seen any eagles there himself, but emphasises the fact that most of the older inhabitants testified as to the presence of eagles in Snowdonia up until 1690 or thereabouts. Rowlands, however, did not accompany Lhuyd on his travels through the Celtic countries in 1697, and there is no evidence of any further involvement in matters of natural history; in 1701 he became vicar of Conwy.

One of Edward Lhuyd's most loyal supporters was his close friend John Lloyd of Blaen y ddôl, Corwen (1662-1725); a keen botanist and a knowledgeable antiquary who possessed a wealth of knowledge about the history of his native locality. Lhuyd was related to John Lloyd and often referred to him as his 'kinsman' in his letters. John Lloyd went up to Oxford about the same time as Lhuyd, and his name later appears in the Subscription Book of the Diocese of St Asaph after being ordained Deacon on 18 December 1686, and Priest on 4 September 1687. By 1689 he was Rector of Llangar, but he removed to Rhuthun in 1691 where Lhuyd addressed his letters to him thus. 'John Lloyd, scholemaster of Ruthyn.' According to J.E. Griffith's *Pedigrees of Anglesey and Carnarvonshire* John Lloyd was buried on 27 February 1725, having died at the age of 63.

John Lloyd visited Snowdonia during the summer of 1686 in the company of John Wynne (1667-1743; Bishop of St Asaph 1716-27). The journey is described in a letter John Lloyd later wrote to Edward Lhuyd. The passage between Llanrwst and Llanberis must have been quite harrowing, and the land over which they had to travel was described as 'ye Divels bowling green'. Snowdon itself was 'one of ye nearest places to Heaven yt is in this World', and their lodgings at Llanberis 'afforded us but cold entertainm't our fare being next to ye worst of a Souldiers. Their best bread being black, tough & thick oatbread wch we had not been much accustom'd to'. John Lloyd hired one of the local guides that had served Edward Lhuyd to lead him to the summit of Snowdon, and the journey most probably began at Nant Peris, which in those days would have been called Llanberis. The plants which had been collected on the way up are described using the long winded pre-Linnean fashion, but some of the names are not difficult to recognize however; *Gramen Parnassi* = the grass-of-Parnassus (*Parnassia palustris*).

Mist and cloud hung over the mountain that day and the guide was reluctant to let the party wander more than the distance of one foot from the path for fear of them getting lost. Somewhere along the way they recorded the stag's-horn club-moss (*Lycopodium clavatum*). When the guide informed the party that they were about a mile from the top and directly above a 'great pool', they persuaded him to allow them to search the surrounding area for plants to within earshot of the guide. Handicapped by poor visibility and the restriction imposed upon them by the guide, the number of plants seen amounted to a surprising 40, and among this rather vaguely described total a single sea-plant is noted. Then the cold damp mountain mist began to affect John Wynne and the guide, and John Lloyd himself had to keep himself warm by rigorous exercise. 'That was ye highest degree of cold yt ever I felt', he complained, and John Wynne had to remove his boots so that he could rub some circulation back into his numbed feet. The guide also advised John Lloyd not to drink from the spring about a mile from the summit in case the coldness of the water caused his teeth to drop out. After the day on Snowdon the party must have been glad to reach the valley once again, but it was plain to them that the way of life of the inhabitants of Snowdonia was far below the standards to which they were accustomed. 'I need not describe Llanberrys parish to you, in wch ne're miller, fuller & any other trades-man but one taylor lives; there [-] a cock, hen or goose, nay ne're an oven in ye Parish.'

John Lloyd made another interesting observation during this visit. He mentions a low circular wall built on the very apex of Snowdon, the purpose of which was to give shelter to those who had walked to the top. 'There is a wall rais'd on ye top of ye Hill, made like a sheepfold where we shelter'd for a while, & carved our names in stones as several others had done before us, for we were as willing to be famouse as they'. There is no conclusive evidence to show when the practice of walking the hills of Snowdonia first began, but it seems almost certain that the custom of climbing to the summit of Snowdon to see the view or the sunrise began quite early in history. According to John Lloyd's testimony, the names carved on the stones of the low circular wall dated from an earlier period than 1686, and this custom was mirrored in the visitors books of the 19th century, by which time wooden cabins had been erected on the summit to provide visitors with food and shelter. The Reverend R.H. Newell in his book *Letters on the Scenery of Wales* (1821) describes a visit to Snowdon undertaken several years before the first cabins were built and notes this curious habit visitors have of wishing to leave their names behind on the summit. 'It is amusing to observe the anxiety of the adventurers to record their exploit; scraps of paper are carefully packed among stones at the top with their names and the date of their excursion'.

Some of the pressed plant specimens of Edward Lhuyd which are preserved in the Morisonian Herbarium at the University of Oxford are signed 'D. Lhwyd', and this might be taken as an error for E. Llwyd, but John Lloyd of Blaenyddol had two brothers, David, the eldest, and Robert. The eldest of the three brothers stayed at Blaen y ddôl while John went up to Oxford, and Robert to London as an apprentice apothecary, and later practised at Wrexham. Following his plant hunting excursions into Snowdonia during the 1680s Edward Lhuyd then left instructions for David Lloyd to carry on the work, so could this then be the reason for the 'D. Lhwyd' which appears on the Herbarium sheets? It would appear not. 'D' was an abbreviation of *Dominus*, the Latin for either Lord, Master, College Professor, or perhaps 'learned gentleman'. It should not, therefore, be read as an initial, but rather as an abbreviation more or less synonymous with mister, (Mr.). David Lloyd proved to be a quick learner and in a letter to Edward Lhuyd, John has this to say in praise of his brother. 'I found my Brother David a greater proficient in plants yn you or I ever expected. He knows most of common plants (like myself) by sight if not by their names'. This is how Edward Lhuyd gave plant hunting directions to David Lloyd. 'It's observable yt on most of these high hills, ye rarest plants & greatest variety are to be met with, by the rivulets of water that descend through the rocks from ye tops of 'm. In goeing up to most of 'm you must make use of a Guide; who must not direct you the easiest way of goeing up; but must bring you to all the steep & craggie cliffs, yt are (tho but difficulty) accessible. You must have a pretty large simpling Book with a stif cover; & be sure of half a dozen patterns of each plant you meet with on these high Hills, in what posture soever you finde 'm. I judge it better worth a mans while goeing to Snowdon alone; than if he search'd all other Hills in North Wales.'

David Lloyd also collected fossils and shells as well as plants for Edward Lhuyd, who collated all this information from local naturalists to be included in his great work.

Of all the botanists mentioned in this chapter pride of place must surely go to Edward Lhuyd for his outstanding contributions to the botanical exploration of Snowdonia. He was also far in advance of his time on his archeological, philological and palaentological thinking as well.

The Diary of Samuel Brewer
and the Lost Manuscript of William Morris

It is interesting how knowledge of the localities of the plants of Snowdonia have been passed on from generation to generation. This has been a tradition from the earliest times when the Druids and the monks and later the herbalists and apothecaries went out into the countryside collecting plants for medicinal purposes; the botanists studied them for more scientific reasons. It was thus transmitted as part of our folk-tradition.

The Reverend Thomas Evans was Vicar of Llanberis parish from 1680 until 1723 when he drowned while returning home late from a Christening ceremony. He was caught in a fierce storm while rowing across one of the Llanberis lakes and the boat overturned: his body was never recovered despite repeated searches.

The Reverend Evans had guided Richard Richardson (1663-1741) and probably Edward Lhuyd (1660-1709), both mentioned earlier, to the plant localities on Glyder and Snowdon. William Griffith also acted as guide. During the month of August 1726, the German botanist Johann Jacob Dillenius (1684-1747) who was the first Sherardian Professor of Botany at Oxford, 1734-47, came to Snowdonia primarily to study the lower plants, such as mosses, liverworts, fungi and algae. Samuel Brewer (1670-1743) accompanied Dillenius on this visit. Brewer, whose woollen manufacturing business at Trowbridge, Wiltshire, had become unsuccessful, turned his interests to natural history and was ranked highly by Dillenius as a plant collector. 'I am sure I shall never meet with a better searcher, especially for mosses. When we travelled together in Wales in all the badness and violency of weather and rain he would stop and pick up mosses.' Brewer stayed in North Wales for twelve months following Dillenius' departure.

Richardson was informed of Dillenius' forthcoming journey into Wales by William Sherard, (1658/9-1728, founder of the Sherardian Chair of Botany at Oxford), and Richardson responded by writing a letter giving details of plants and their localities and directions as to finding them.

Armed with Richardson's letter of directions, Dillenius and Brewer entered Wales near Newtown, and rode to Dolgellau via Llanidloes. Here they climbed Cadair Idris. They then spent six days on Anglesey and crossed the Straits back to Caernarfon, then proceeding towards Snowdon, making Llanberis their base.

On 20 August they ascended Snowdon by way of Cwmglas Mawr and continued towards the summit from Bwlch Coch by traversing Crib y Ddisgl. Water lobelia (*Lobelia dortmanna*) and quillwort (*Isoetes lacustris*) were recorded from the lakes of Cwmglas Mawr, and mountain sorrel (*Oxyria digyna*) parsley fern (*Cryptogramma crispa*) lesser clubmoss (*Selaginella selaginoides*) alpine meadow-rue (*Thalictrum alpinum*) and moss campion (*Silene acaulis*) from the cliffs further up. The alpine mouse-ear (*Cerastium alpinum*) was then, as now, a rare flower in Snowdonia, but the party recorded this during their ascent, most probably from the north-east facing cliffs of the main Snowdon peak where the plant has been occasionally found by later botanists. When they reached the summit of Snowdon they found the mis-named Iceland 'moss', which is in fact a lichen (*Cetraria islandica*), and which still grows among the rocks near the summit. It appears that the weather which had been fine for most of the day suddenly took a turn for the worse, and they returned to Llanberis after a long day out.

The two botanists went up Glyder Fawr on 22 August and Dillenius' account confirms the use that was made of Richardson's letter. 'According to the directions we could not find the Hieracium said to grow there, nor the Virga aurea.' The plants here referred to are most probably the alpine hawkweed (*Hieracium holosericeum*) and the goldenrod (*Solidago virgaurea*). What they did find however, turned out to be the rarest clubmoss in Snowdonia, the interrupted clubmoss (*Lycopodium annotinum*) a plant that has not been seen in the area since the first half of the 19th century. It was first found by Lhuyd and recorded in Camden's *Britannia* (1695). On 23 August the two botanists rested and sorted through the plant specimens they had gathered on Snowdon and Glyder. According to Richard Pulteney's *Historical and biological sketches of the progress of botany in England* (1790), Dillenius then left Wales and went to Ireland, but Samuel Brewer decided to stay for another year in North Wales based mainly at Bangor.

Brewer botanised extensively in Caernarfonshire and Anglesey between 26 February and 24 September 1727, and his activities are recorded in a personal Diary. He climbed Snowdon thirteen times and made seven excursions to the Glyder mountains collecting plant specimens and forwarding them to Dillenius who had agreed to name them in exchange for keeping a full set and duly returning the remainder to the collector.

There is no evidence as to the existence of Samuel Brewer's original Diary, but a manuscript copy in the hand of the Reverend Hugh Davies (1739-1821) is kept at the Department of Botany, National Museum of Wales, Cardiff, and a similar transcript but with slight variation in the hand of Sigismund Bacstrom is in the Department of Botany, Natural History Museum, Cromwell Road, London which bears the signature of Sir Joseph Banks (1743-1820) on the title page.

Another eminent Welsh botanist of the period, John Wynne Griffith of Y Garn, Henllan near Denbigh (1763-1834) is known to have had a copy of Brewer's Diary with him when he came on a botanizing visit to the Llanberis area during the 1790s. The custom of borrowing and copying from botanical manuscripts dates from the time of the herbalists when remedies were noted

*Map showing the places
visited by Brewer in 1726-7
(courtesy of the National
Museum of Wales)*

and circulated in a similar manner.

The home of the Reverend Thomas Evans had been vacant following his tragic death, and Dillenius and Brewer did not have the benefit of staying with the hospitable local Vicar, as Richardson and others did during their visits to Llanberis. The pair had therefore to put up at 'a very hard and uncomfortable lodging at the alehouse'. It also proved difficult at first to obtain the services of a guide, and the language presented additional problems. William Evans, the late Vicar's son, was at the time living in Bangor, and on hearing about the visitors' predicament he immediately made available his old home at Llanberis and provided food and fuel for the visiting botanists. William Evans at a later date succeeded his father as Vicar of Llanberis.

Following Dillenius' departure from North Wales, Brewer appreciated even more the support of William Evans, who in turn introduced him to William Jones of Llanfaethlu, Anglesey and the Reverend William Green; these two men were Brewer's most constant companions during his botanical excursions.

Another of Brewer's guides was Richard Parry who led the botanist to Clogwyn Du'r Arddu to search the cave there for ferns, but alas, this guide did not come up to the mark as the following passage from the Diary reads 'I was forced to part with R. Parry who would not follow me upon the rocks.'

35

The rarer species of flowering plants and ferns which Brewer records from the Eryri mountains had been observed by earlier botanists, but many of the commoner species noted in the Diary appear to be first records. The reason for this is that the earlier travellers were only interested in plants which were new to them, and subsequently the ones that they were already familiar with were not noted. The mosses and lichens collected and listed by Brewer, many of which were previously unknown, are very difficult to identify and translate into modern terms. Brewer when noting all the plants, used the cumbersome pre-Linnean practice where each species is described in full. For instance the alpine saxifrage (*Saxifraga nivalis*) was written thus: '*Saxifraga foliis oblongis rotundis dentatis, floribus compactis*', and quotes the abbreviated title of the work to which he refers (i.e. 'R.S' = Ray's Synopsis). Students wishing to identify the flowering plants and ferns referred to by Brewer are able to do so by consulting the Dillenian Herbaria at the Department of Plant Sciences, University of Oxford.

On 17 August, Brewer, accompanied by William Jones and the Reverend William Green, walked up Snowdon and gathered seeds from the choice plants which they found to be ripe. The diarist states that he met with no plants that were not already known to him except the '*Filix alpina pedicularis rubrae folio, subtus villosa*', which in modern terms is known as the alpine woodsia (*Woodsia alpina*), one of the rarer ferns. The site of this fern which grows on the cliffs of Clogwyn y Garnedd, Snowdon, is extant today, but can only be reached with some difficulty. Brewer also experienced difficulties in trying to obtain specimens of the fern and they 'were forced to take them down with a pole twenty feet long with a radicator at its end'. Brewer describes the specimen taken as being 'past its beauty and mostly in a withered state'. The woodsia ferns normally remain in good state throughout the summer and autumn but will begin to wither when the first frosts of winter attack them. During a prolonged dry spell, however, the fronds will shrink causing the plant to appear lifeless, but a shower of rain will soon revive them.

Brewer credits the Reverend William Green as being the first member of the party to find the '*Woodsia*' on the day. The Reverend William Green (d.1782) was curate at Bodedern, Anglesey, during the years 1725-6 and was later rector at Llanfair Dyffryn Clwyd. He was the son of Jeremiah Green of Dublin and Ann, the daughter of William Williams, the owner of Castellmai near Caernarfon. Details of the family's geneology appear in Griffith's *Pedigrees &c*, under the heading 'Plas Pentir'. Ten of the plant specimens collected by William Green are preserved in the *Synopsis* Herbarium, and one in the *Historia Muscorum* of the Dillenian Herbarium, at the University of Oxford. They include three specimens of algae, one moss and six flowering plants, three of which are from Snowdonia.

Small-white orchid (*Pseudorchis albida*) 'from ye meadows at Nant

Francon . . . '

Darnel (*Lolium temulentum*) which was the first record for Caernarfonshire of the awned form of this grass. 'Yeed Meddw which signify drunken corn . . . '

Field gentian (*Gentianella campestris*) 'In a meadow calld Talgai near & south from Llanberis church in ye stony ground where ye river formerly ran . . . [also] from Anglesey, Mr Green.' This being the earliest Oxford record of this plant.

There are four specimens from William Jones in the Dillenian Herbarium of the *Synopsis* and all are species of algae collected from Anglesey. They are *Plocamium coccineum* (2 sheets), *Delesseria alata* and *Chylocladia ovatus*.

William Griffith guided Brewer on 10 July to the unidentified 'Trigyfylchau Rocks' to look for the Snowdon lily (*Lloydia serotina*), but despite the fact that they followed the instructions set by Richardson in his letter the plant was not found. William Griffith, who had previously guided Richardson to the site swore that they were on the very rock where the *Lloydia* grew. Normally this plant is only in flower for a couple of weeks between late May and mid June, and after that time only the long rush like leaves remain, which, as previously stated, could easily be overlooked or mistaken for a clump of grass.

Samuel Brewer is credited as being the first to record the spotted rock-rose in Britain, and he was duly honoured in the earlier name of the plant *Helianthemum Breweri*. The true finder of the plant was in fact the Reverend William Green, who gathered specimens of it from Holyhead mountain and sent them to Brewer, who in due course passed them on to Dillenius at Oxford. The true circumstances under which the plant was found were never revealed, and Dillenius upon receiving the specimens from Brewer decided to name the plant in honour of its 'discoverer'. Proof that the spotted rock-rose (now named *Tuberaria guttata*) was a new plant recorded for Britain appear in a letter from Dillenius to Brewer dated 31 May 1727 where the Professor requests that the Reverend Green looks for more specimens of the flower and concludes. 'It is a Cistus and seems to be new'.

The last entry in Samuel Brewer's Diary is that of 24 September, and by November he was staying with Dr Richardson at his home in North Brierley near Bradford in Yorkshire which suggests that he had taken the advice of Dillenius in a letter to him dated 30 September to 'get out of the difficult country before the bad weather set in'.

Samuel Brewer, unlike most of the visiting botanists to North Wales, was not of the higher station of society, but his contributions to botany were certainly held in high regard by Dr Richardson and other contemporary botanists. According to the *Dictionary of National Biography*, Brewer later became head gardener to the Duke of Beaufort at Badminton, following a period of his life when he fell on hard times. His valuable collection of plants and seaweeds which had been pressed and dried by himself were purchased for

£20 shortly before his death by Richard Richardson, which proves how low his circumstances were; previously he had refused an offer of £100 from Sir Hans Sloane for his collection. He died in 1743 at Brierley, and was buried at Cleckheaton; the precise date is not known.

William Morris (1705-1763), one of the famous Morris Brothers of Anglesey was a notable botanist who belonged to the period currently dealt with. The Morris Brothers had a remarkable range of interests which are reflected in their correspondence; these letters were published in parts by J.H. Davies between 1907 and 1909 and by Hugh Owen through the Honourable Society of Cymmrodorion in 1947 and 1949. The letters provide an informative picture of life in Anglesey and other parts of North Wales during the 18th century.

William Morris refers to his botanical interests in his letters and his garden at Holyhead is also constantly mentioned. 'I dont remember whether ever I told you that I've for upwards of three years been a-studying botany. I've made a catalogue in English, Welsh, and Latin of the plants growing in and about Holyhead, where we have a great many pretty rare ones'. (M.L. 14 October 1740).

William Morris was appointed Deputy Comptroller of the Customs at Holyhead in 1737, to which he later added other duties, and unlike his brothers Lewis and Richard who left the island to earn a living, he remained in Anglesey. Lewis became a surveyor engaged by the Admiralty to survey the coasts of Wales, and in 1746 he was appointed Deputy Steward of the Crown Manors in Cardiganshire. Richard lived in London where he worked as an accountant, looking after the interests of prominent citizens of the capital, and, through the influence of his clients he later obtained a post in the Admiralty.

William Morris must have inherited his mother's natural flair of knowing the native plants of Anglesey. Margaret Morris was known throughout the island as a knowledgeable herbalist and she had a Welsh name for all the plants. William, too, had quite a reputation as a local doctor, and his services were called upon frequently as were his mother's before him.

Several names of famous botanists appear in his letters, names such as John Ray, James Lee, Benjamin Stillingfleet and Phillip Miller, the curator of the Chelsea Physic Garden, and many notable naturalists and members of the local gentry came to see his garden.

He published a book entitled *The Kitchen, Fruit and Flower Gardens Complete* in Dublin in 1751; the only known copy is in a private collection in Cardiff, and in the 1979 issue of the *Transactions of the Honourable Society of Cymmrodorion* the book, together with the 18th century manuscripts that were bound with it, were published by William Linnard and Robin Gwyndaf. The volume was first brought to the attention of the writers in 1976, and it was evident to them upon examination that it was a very rare work. The printed

The Old Physic Garden of the Society of Apothecaries at Chelsea, 1750.

book is anonymous, with no indication as to how many copies were published, and no mention is made of the book in any of the letters that passed between the brothers. There can be no question that the manuscripts were written by William Morris, and it would appear that the book is by the same author.

The information compiled in the book has been divided into four parts and presents advice on the Kitchen Garden, the Fruit Garden, and lastly two equally divided parts on the Flower Garden. The nineteen manuscript pages which were bound into the front part of the volume consist mainly of a gardener's calendar and thirteen pages of the twenty-one that were bound to the back form an index to the work.

As already stated, there is no mention of this gardening book in any of the Morris Brother's letters, but William Morris informs his brother Richard in a letter written on 2 January 1746 of a local 'flora' he had been preparing which he calls '*Botanologium*'. This, most probably, is the 'catalogue' mentioned previously on page 38. The names of plants would appear he says in Welsh, Latin, English and Irish, but no further information has been noted as to the outcome of this work. Sixty-seven years later another Anglesey botanist, the Reverend Hugh Davies (1739-1821) acknowledged William Morris in his book *Welsh Botanology* which was published in 1813. 'In the neighbourhood of Holyhead' he writes on page vii, 'I see much done in that way in the hand-writing of that good practical botanist, and proficient in the British language, Mr William Morris, some time ago Comptroller of his Majesty's Customs at that place; and especially in a MS by him which bears the title 'A Collection of Plants gathered in Anglesey'. This work was never published and the original manuscript later came into the possession of William Morris' daughter who lived in Beaumaris. The Reverend Hugh Davies also lived in Beaumaris during this time and he no doubt borrowed the manuscript for consultation while working on his Anglesey Flora, *Welsh Botanology*, but since that time there has been no trace of it.

The middle years of the 18th century saw a major development in the Science of botany. John Ray and Edward Lhuyd had previously tried to perfect a system of naming plants by grouping those which were related, but the system remained awkward and complicated. Botany was in dire need of a simple method by which they could sort into order, identify and name plants. Carolus Linnaeus (1707-1778) created such a system. His book, *Species Plantarum*, published in 1753, includes all the plants then known to science, and they are listed in order of the new classification scheme based on number and arrangement of the sex organs of the flower. In addition he gave each plant a name consisting of two words only. The long descriptive Latin phrase by which plants had been named up until this time was retained as a description but replaced as a name by two words; the genus which the plant belongs to first, followed by a descriptive name to distinguish it from all other species of the same genus; a system analogue to our use of forenames and surnames. Botany benefited as a result of the Linnean System, and the cataloguing of the flora of a country became much easier.

William Morris visited Snowdon on 17 June 1741 and listed seventeen plants that he saw there; worsening weather conditions however, made any further searching impracticable. He was accompanied on this trip by several friends, some of whom rode from Anglesey with him while the others had arranged to meet them at Hafodty in Cwmbrwynog at the foot of Snowdon. His companions are named as being the Reverend Thomas Ellis of Holyhead, the Reverend Henry Williams of Caernarfon, Mr Phillip Quellyn (d.1782 a customs officer at Caernarfon) of Cwellyn, Betws Garmon, Mr Richard Owen of Isallt (Holyhead?) and Mr Hugh Jones (1706-1757) of Cymunod, Bodedern, Anglesey. The name 'Rolant o Gwm Brwynog' is also included with the above and this local man could well have acted as guide to the party. The above names have been extracted from a manuscript in the hand of William Morris which is kept at the National Library of Wales, (N.L.W. Ms 6666) in which the writer has copied a lengthy list of alpine plants which were published in Camden's *Britannia* (1695). 'This catalogue I drew out to assist me in finding out the Plants therein mentioned when I went a Simpling a top of Snowdon 17th June 1741 & may save [serve?] future searches'.

The name Snowdon lily (*Lloydia serotina*) does not appear among the plants which William Morris lists as having seen on Snowdon, but he can claim to be the first to give it the Welsh names of 'brwynddail y mynydd' and 'y bryfedog'. The first name signifies 'rush-leaved mountain plant', and the second is a loose translation of the English name 'spiderwort'. These names are to be found among a long list of Welsh plant names which were written by William Morris on the margins and plain pages of the *'Botanology'* section of his personal copy of Thomas Richards' Dictionary entitled *Antiquae linguae Britannicae thesaurus* (1753). It would appear from reading an annotation on the first page of the *'Botanology'* part that William Morris had offered to make the necessary corrections to the work prior to it being printed, but Richards had declined the offer. The amendments and additions which William Morris made are considerable and appear on every page in this particular chapter. Such a wealth of plant names was most certainly collected for the purpose of forming his *Botanologium*, the fate of which remains unknown. The dictionary, which is preserved at the British Library, (Additional Ms 14947) possibly contains most of the information recorded in the lost manuscript, other than any plant localities that the botanist may have added. It is known that William Morris made at least one more visit to Snowdon. In a letter to his brother Richard dated 23 August 1754 he notes his disappointment at not being able to go botanizing in Snowdonia that summer with his friend Owen Holland of Plas Isa, Conwy (1720-1795) who was also a keen botanist. Another letter to Richard dated 2 March 1756 confirms William Morris' second botanical excursion to Snowdon. 'Had a letter from him [Thomas Pennant] last Saturday, and the same time another from Mr Lysons, of Hemsted, in Gloucestershire; an ingenious gentleman, who was with us at Snowdon last summer.' Botany remained one of William Morris' main interests throughout his life and in June 1763, he was considering an invitation by Owen Holland to accompany him on a visit to Snowdonia that summer. William Morris died six months later, on 29 December.

John Wynne Griffith of Garn and his Contemporaries

Dawson Turner (1775-1858), who in 1835 published the *Extracts from the Literary and Scientific Correspondence of Richard Richardson*, states in a footnote on page 237 how he wished he could have had a copy of Richardson's letter of directions to Dillenius and Brewer with him in 1802. Turner was probably referring to a visit to Snowdonia he made in that year to collect plant records for a book he and Lewis Weston Dillwyn (1778-1855) published in 1805 entitled *The Botanist's Guide through England and Wales*. The book, which consists of two volumes, catalogues all the then-known plants of each county in England and Wales. It was probably the first book to appear in print which dealt exclusively with plant distribution on a county by county basis. The *Botanist's Guide* was not based upon the observations of the authors alone, but rather on the work of local botanists, and on plant records which had been previously published. The Caernarfonshire plants are to a large extent entered on the authority of two of the leading Welsh botanists of the period, the Reverend Hugh Davies (1739-1821) and John Wynne Griffith (1763-1834). The Reverend Hugh Davies is well known for his work in compiling his personal botanical observations and publishing them in his *Welsh Botanology*, which

John Wynne Griffith (1763-1834)

42

appeared in 1813. John Wynne Griffith, on the other hand, had none of his work published, but permitted other writers to make known his findings. The Reverend William Bingley published a number of Griffith's records in the appendix of his book *North Wales including its Scenery, Antiquities Customs &c* in 1800 under the heading '*Flora Cambrica*', but only once is Griffith's name mentioned by the author. 'Mr Griffith of Garn, whose judgement on botanical subjects is of great weight . . . ' he states, (page 406, 1804 ed) before continuing with the problems raised by a plant he calls 'Alpine Hedypnois', but which Griffith dismisses as being just a variety of the autumn hawkbit (*Leontodon autumnalis*).

John Wynne Griffith was born on 1 April 1763, at Wig, near Aber in Caernarfonshire. He was the son of John Griffith of Garn near Denbigh and Jane the daughter of John Hughes of Wig, Caernarfonshire and Cae'r Berllan near Llanrwst. John Wynne Griffith was at Trinity Hall, Cambridge in 1781. He was married in 1785 to Jane, the daughter of Robert Wynne, Garthmeilo and Plasnewydd, and they had thirteen children. In 1806 he supported Robert Biddulph as candidate against his brother in law, Frederick West, and in 1812 led the Whig faction supporting Biddulph in the election, but without success. He was returned to Parliament in 1818 as M.P. for Denbigh and remained a staunch supporter of the Whig opposition. He was a keen supporter of any agricultural improvement, but was not prominent in debate. He retired in 1826 and died on 20 June 1834.

Griffith, as already mentioned, assisted other botanists by providing them with details of his own observations. William Withering acknowledges Griffith's help in his book *Arrangement of British Plants* (1796 vol.i page ix) and names 'J.W. Griffith whose numerous and instructive specimens and observations have greatly enriched the catalogue of Mosses and Lichens'. Griffith, whose great speciality was lichens, had also a keen interest in the 'tall' plants and is credited with being the first to record the wild cotoneaster (*Cotoneaster cambricus*) from the Great Orme, Llandudno in 1783, and also the tufted saxifrage (*Saxifraga cespitosa*) from Cwm Idwal in 1778. A hitherto unknown moss which he found on Snowdon in 1790 was named in his honour, and the *Oedipodium griffithianum* still flourishes on the eastern side of the summit where it was first discovered.

In 1830 John Williams (1801-1859), doctor and naturalist, published a list of plants, animals and birds which are found in the parish of Llanrwst in the Conwy Valley under the title *Faunula Grustensis*. The author dedicated the book to John Wynne Griffith of whom he wrote 'The last mentioned Gentleman, who is still living (at Garn near Denbigh) I have had occasion to name him frequently in the Catalogue of Indigenous Plants; as he in his younger days explored the productions of all the mountains and valleys in North Wales, and therefore he is acquainted with the habitats of the rare plants: Although he has the genius of Pennant, yet instead of imitating him, he communicated the fruit of his labours to other writers'. It would therefore appear that John Wynne Griffith did not wish to make a name for himself as a politician or a botanist.

John Wynne Griffith visited Snowdon in 1804 accompanied by his friend William Withering and in an entry made in the Capel Curig Inn's visitors book on 24 October they describe a rare phenomenom they experienced whilst ascending the mountain. 'Arriving half past six evening; at half past seven the following morning we set off for Cwm Dyli which we reached by nine, after resting half an hour we began to ascend Snowdon, the summit of which we attained by half past one . . . what chiefly deserves to be recorded was a beautiful natural Phenomenom hitherto we believe seen by few which repeatedly presented itself. This curious spectacle is known to Philosophers by the name of Glory and is . . . described by Dr Haygarth late of Chester but now of Bath in a paper published a few years ago. It consists of a beautiful and splendid prismatic annulus in the centre of which your own figure, considerably larger than life is presented. This unusual appearance as may be supposed produced the most awful and sublime Ideas. We experienced every civility from the Host and Hostess. N.B. The want of bells was the only thing we had to complain of.'

J.W. Griffith was introduced to Sir Joseph Banks (1743-1820), in 1783 in a letter written by John Lloyd (1749-1815), of the families of Wig-fair and Hafodunnos in Clwyd; Lloyd had been corresponding with Banks regularly between 1778 and 1790, chiefly discussing geology and botany. The letter of introduction reads 'a very near neighbour of mine, a very goodnatured young man of family and a decent fortune, now at Cambridge, quite an enthusiast in Botany and very desirous of being introduced to you . . . ' The letter is headed 'Wickwar' which is undoubtedly an error in transcription for 'Wig-fair', the residence of John Lloyd near St Asaph.

The only letter from Griffith in the Banksian Correspondence is dated 12 July 1802 and is concerned with the discovery by the writer of a shell fish called Periwinkle which 'is only the first state of a small species of Lobster', and goes on to say that the discovery will 'astonish the world'. There is no mention of botany and the letter is written in a very formal manner which suggests that Griffith did not have a prolonged or close relationship with Banks. Griffith became a Fellow of the Linnean Society on the recommendation of James Dickson and Thomas Markham; the certificate is dated 24 May 1795. Griffith sent plant specimens in a tin box to James Sowerby together with a letter dated 28 May 1797. Sowerby (1757-1822) was a botanical artist who engraved the plates for J.E. Smith's *English Botany*, a 36 volumed work which was published between 1790 and 1814. The Sowerby material is kept at the Natural History Museum, in eighty-five large boxes, and the one letter from J.W.

Griffith is rather interesting.

Garn near Denbigh,
May 28th 1797.

'Sir. I have sent you at the request of Dr Smith by this Days Mail the following Plants as numbered below to be engraved for the English Botany. They are packed up in a tin Box, & I hope they will come safe to hand.

I am Sir Your obedt servant
J.W. Griffith.

No. 1. Cerastium latifolium [Arctic mouse-ear (*Cerastium arcticum*)]
No. 2. Cerastium alpinum [Alpine mouse-ear (*Cerastium alpinum*)]
No. 3. Draba incana [Hoary whitlowgrass]
No. 4. Saxifraga petraea * [perhaps a variety, or an error for S.hypnoides]
No. 5. Saxifraga perhaps near, or a variety of S.hypnoides
No. 6. Cardamine petraea [Northern rock-cress (*Arabis petraea*)]
No. 7. Sax. nivalis [Alpine saxifrage (*Saxifraga nivalis*)]
No. 8. Serratula alpina [Alpine saw-wort (*Saussurea alpina*)]
No. 9. Rhodiola rosea [Roseroot (*Sedum rosea*)]
No.10. Salix herbacea with catkins [Dwarf willow]
and Sax hypnoides at top unlabelled.

8 & 9 are not come into flower, but I hope you will be able to flower them in water. When you have done with the specimens I shall be obliged to you if you will present them to the person who has the care of the Hortus Siccus of the Linnean Society to whom they may perhaps be acceptable. Pray excuse haste & you may expect to hear further from me concerning their Habitats &c but if in the mean time you are desirous of any information in my Power to communicate, you will please to address J.W. Griffith, Garn near Denbigh, N. Wales'.

* In the *Arrangement of British Plants* by William Withering (1796, vol 3 page 890) the author acknowledges Griffith's new discovery. 'We are indebted to the indefatigable researches of J. Wynne Griffith, Esq. for this beautiful addition to our Flora. He found it on the rocks of Cwm Idwell, above Llyn Idwell, near Twll Du, and favoured me with recent specimens. It is a very scare plant.'

Sir James Edward Smith (1759-1828) purchased Linnaeus' collections in 1784 and founded the Linnean Society in 1788; he published *Flora Britannica* in three volumes between 1800 and 1804, and wrote the text for *English Botany* to which Sowerby, mentioned earlier, provided the plant drawings. The Smith Herbarium at the Linnean Society contains only one specimen collected by Griffith; 'Saxifraga hypnoides North Wales J.W. Griffith 1796', but there are no specimens of hoary whitlowgrass (*Draba incana*) or alpine saxifrage (*Saxifraga nivalis*) or any of the plants which Griffith sent to Sowerby, according to the microfiche of the Smith Herbarium which is available at the Natural History Museum.

Sowerby's plate of a drawing of the Snowdon lily (*Lloydia serotina*) which appears in *English Botany* (page 793) was taken from a specimen collected in Snowdonia by J.W. Griffith and sent to Smith. There is also a sheet of *Lloydia* in the Banksian Herbarium at the Natural History Museum endorsed by Joseph Banks, 'Trig-y-fylichan, [Trigyfylchau] part of the Glyder Range on the N. side of Llanberris in the County of Carnarvon, found by J.W. Griffith of Garn Esq., the 23rd of June 1794.'

John Lloyd had also sent a specimen of '*Lloydia*' to Banks and the latter replied and stated that he was not convinced about the identity of the plant in question. Lloyd's answer written on 1 October 1778 reads: 'I was much surprised to find you were not satisfied of the bulbose plant I sent being Bulbocodium [*Lloydia serotina*] I do not recollect ever before having seen any plant with a bulbose root near Llanberris; and the leaves answered the description very exactly, so I hope, upon the whole, you may be mistaken; it grew deep betwixt a cleft in the rock which was moist facing the north, with a great deal of earth about the root, which lay 4 inches under the splinter of the rock.' John Wynne Griffith had also acquired a copy of Brewer's Diary and had spent some time in the neighbourhood of Llanberis in 1790 when he found all the plants that were recorded in the Diary by the old botanist. Griffith, however, found many of the place names changed or forgotten since Brewer's day, but he managed to locate the habitats of the rare plants by consulting the journal and by seeking local help. According to John Lloyd, writing to Banks on 28 November 1790, Griffith 'had made a very fine and plentiful collection now in his garden' from the plants he had gathered during this excursion, of which the rare '*Lloydia*' was one.

John Lloyd was a regular visitor to Snowdonia during the latter part of the 18th century; he was known as 'the Philosopher' and was one of the many 'dilettantes' of the time. Among his many interests were geology and botany, and whenever he went on one of his field trips to Snowdon he took Hugh Jones of Cwmglas Bach with him as guide. It is also said that John Lloyd publicised the name of Hugh Jones in the newspapers of the period as a guide who could be relied on to give satisfactory service. This same guide probably served J.W. Griffith.

Sir Joseph Banks' interest in obtaining specimens of '*Lloydia*' first becomes apparent in a letter that the Reverend John Lightfoot (1735-1788) wrote him on 19 June 1773. Banks and Lightfoot visited Wales during the summer of that year, but Lightfoot was at first doubtful if he would be free to make the journey. 'If I should be so unfortunate as not to have it in my Power to accompany you, I will take the Liberty to rely on you for a specimen of the Bulbocodium serotinum [*Lloydia serotina*] which I have no doubt of your finding Lightfoot's journal gives an account of the journey made through Wales by the two botanists. The transcript of the original journal was written by Daniel Carl Solander (1733-1782) and is kept at the Natural History Museum.

They arrived at Llanberis at the beginning of August and ascended Snowdon on the 2nd, gathering various specimens of flowering plants, mosses and lichens. The ease by which the visiting botanists found rarities such as the alpine saxifrage (*Saxifraga nivalis*) arctic mouse-ear (*Cerastium arcticum*) and the alpine saw-wort (*Saussurea alpina*) suggests that they were led to the localities by a local botanist, or by one of the guides. Their quest to find the Snowdon lily (*Lloydia serotina*) failed on the 4th and the 5th of August when the party went firstly to Glyder and then to Clogwyn Du'r Arddu in the company of the Reverend John Williams, Rector of Llanfair yng Nghornwy, Anglesey, who is mentioned by the Reverend Hugh Davies in his '*Welsh Botanology*' (1813) on page 53. The flowering time of the *Lloydia* was well over by this time and like plant hunters before them the elusive lily had foiled them also.

The botanists then crossed over to Anglesey finding the Isle of Man cabbage (*Coincya monensis ssp monensis*) and marram (*Ammophila arenaria*) near Abermenai Ferry, and Portland spurge (*Euphorbia portlandica*) at Llanddwyn. On the shore at Llanfaelog they found small quantities of cottonweed (*Otanthus maritimus*) then continued their journey to Llanfair yng Nghornwy and Cemlyn Bay, before returning to the mainland; there to follow the coast to Conwy and Gloddaeth, near Llandudno, where they stayed with Sir Roger Mostyn before continuing their journey to Chester.

Banks' Welsh tour followed his voyages of discovery, and he will always be associated with Captain Cook's voyage around the world on the *Endeavour* between the years 1768 and 1771. His journey through Wales with Lightfoot is considered to be the last of the historic botanical expeditions to North Wales; the original plan of which was to follow in the footsteps of John Ray in 1662, but in reverse order. However, due to having spent too much time in Pembrokeshire they had to abandon their plans to visit Cadair Idris so that they could have enough time to explore Snowdon. The journey from St Davids through Hereford and Chester to Bangor and eventually Llanberis took exactly seven days; this was considered good going and was done in much less time than it would have taken, had they followed the rough terrain of the western coast of Wales.

Hugh Davies, The 'Welsh Linnaeus'

The Reverend Hugh Davies, who was mentioned earlier as having a transcript of Brewer's Diary, was the most knowledgeable Welsh botanist since Edward Lhuyd. Among the local people he was known as 'Davies y dail', (Davies the leaves) but to his fellow British botanists he was 'the Welsh Linnaeus'. He was born on 3 April 1739, the son of Lewis Davies, the Vicar of Llandyfrydog, Anglesey, and after attending the Beaumaris Free Grammar School he went up to Oxford, residing at Jesus College. He was still at Oxford when he was ordained deacon in 1763, having graduated B.A. the previous year. In 1764 he was ordained priest by the Bishop of Bangor and in 1768 took his M.A. It became evident from quite early in his career that natural history was to play a major part in his life; indeed, he would hardly be remembered purely for his work as Rector and Curate.

H. Davies (1739-1821)

In 1774 he visited the Isle of Man in the company of Thomas Pennant and other gentlemen of standing. Proof of Davies' dedication to botany is thus noted by the great author. 'I should accuse myself of undue neglect if I did not acknowledge various services I received from the friendship of Mr Davies at different times since the beginning of our acquaintance. I will in particular mention those which resulted from his great knowledge of botany. To him we owe the account of our Snowdonian plants. To him I lie under the obligation that in June 1775 at my request he undertook another voyage to the Isle of Man to take a second review of its vegetable production. By his labours a Flora of the Island is rendered as complete as is possible to be effected by a single person in one season of the year. The number of plants he observed amounted to 500.' (Pennant's *Literary Life &c.* 1793).

Davies is also known to have assisted Pennant with his *Indian Zoology*, a work that was published in 1790.

The Reverend Hugh Davies, it would seem, had ample free time to carry out his botanical researches. During the late 18th century it was customary for rectors, providing they had the means, to pay a curate to carry out the duties of the parish and during his 29 years at Aber near Bangor, where he held the living from 1787 following his period at Llandegfan, Anglesey, he had no fewer than six. He knew the plant distribution of his native Anglesey well, and as Pennant testifies, he was an authority on the alpine plants of Caernarfonshire, and like John Wynne Griffith, Davies supplied Turner and Dillwyn with plant records which they included in their *Botanist's Guide to England and Wales* (1805).

Davies carried out his botanical work during a period in history which was both uncertain and dramatic. The country was troubled by the effects of the French Revolution while other religious denominations were beginning to cause problems for the Church. He is known to have spoken out in no uncertain terms against Noncomformity, but it does not seem to have caused him any major worries. While Sir Thomas Wyn of Glynllifon formed the Caernarfonshire Volunteers and built Fort Williamsburg and Fort Belan on his land, Hugh Davies roamed the hills of Snowdonia and the extensive fens of Anglesey looking for plants.

In 1813 he published the fruits of his labour in a two part volume which was the first Welsh county flora to appear in print. This followed a two-year leave of absence granted him by the Bishop of Bangor during which he busied himself preparing his *Welsh Botanology*. The first part of the book is a catalogue of the native plants of Anglesey, where each plant listed is classified in the Linnean System starting with the genus, and then the specific name, English name and the Welsh name, and in some cases as many as three or four synonyms for the one plant. The names follow the text set by Smith in his *Flora Britannica*. In the Appendix of the first part of the book he listed the 'British Generic Names of those Phoenogamous Plants in Flora Britannica, which are not of spontaneous Growth in Anglesey'. Davies included several of the Snowdonian species in this list and for the first time in print appears the Welsh name of the Snowdon lily (*Lloydia serotina*) which is 'brwynddail y mynydd'. This he no doubt copied from the manuscript *Botanologium* of William Morris mentioned previously. He listed the mountain avens (*Dryas octopetala*) as 'Derig' which is derived from 'derw', (oak), on account of the leaves of the plant being likened to oak leaves. The roseroot (*Sedum rosea*) is called 'Pren y ddannoedd' which implies that the plant was used to cure toothache, and globeflower (*Trollius europaeus*), was called 'Cronell'; the Welsh word for globe.

Following the common names, Davies gives the type of habitat, and names actual localities where some of the more uncommon species are to be found. Each entry then concludes with the flowering time.

The flora was produced years before the first Ordnance Survey maps in

North Wales appeared, and the introduction of the grid line system which made the job of pin-pointing any locality relatively easy and far more precise. These old books however, are of special interest to the local historian, as the localities named, and the comments which follow them, are much more informative in that respect than the modern county floras which replaced them. Here are a few examples.

'Lithospermum arvense. Corn [field] Gromwell . . . in Baron Hill and Red-Hill demesnes, on each side of the road which leads by the Almshouse. Paris quadrifolia Herb Paris. Near Carreg y forwyllt, on the west side of the river near Llangefni. This account I have taken from an old, elegantly-written manuscript.'

The awlwort (*Subularia aquatica*) is a plant which grows in lakes and pools and occurs in highland Snowdonia as well as in some lowland sites. Hugh Davies' early record from Anglesey is worth quoting. 'In the dry summer of 1798, as I walked the bed of a lake called Llyn Llywenan, in the parish of Bodedern, whence the water had retired about two months before, I very unexpectedly discovered this plant in great abundance. Notwithstanding its appearance was very different from what I had been used to see in the Arvonian Alpine lakes, where it always blossoms and seeds at the bottom, under water of considerable depth, yet it did not seem to regret the privation; the foliage was spread, the leaves somewhat reclining, and the flowering stems procumbent; the calyx and corolla were fully expanded; the petals, which are white and of an obovate form, were horizontal, the seed vessels and seed quite perfected; and, on the whole, it seemed to indicate a quite different plant.'

The plant was again recorded from Llyn Llywenan by J.E. Griffith (1894/5), but there have been no recent sightings of it in Anglesey. It still grows in a small lake in Cwmglas Mawr on Snowdon where it was first noted by Edward Lhuyd and published in Camden's *Britannia* (1695). 'A spindle-leav'd Water-Sengreen-like Plant, growing in the bottom of a small Lake near the top of Snowdon hill, call'd Phynon Vrech.'

Hugh Davies in his note on the habitat of the cottonweed (*Otanthus maritimus*) (*Welsh Botanology* p.76.) confirms the use he made of his transcript of Samuel Brewer's Diary. 'This plant is now become very scarce below Llanfaelog, [Anglesey] where Mr Brewer "found it in great plenty for a mile together" on Sept. the 5th. 1727.' A note in his transcript of the Diary reads; '*Gnaphalium maritimum [Otanthus maritimus]* doth not grow anywhere about Abermeney or Llanddwyn whatever it did formerly'. [cf. Ray's statement, "We found it plentifully on the Sand near Abermeney-Ferry, in the Isle of Anglesea"]. Lightfoot however, during his visit with Banks in 1773, records having seen cottonweed 'among the Sands at Llanfaelog on the west Side of the Island . . . ' Brewer's Diary is again mentioned following his notes on the sea stock (*Matthiola sinuata*). Davies includes the plant on the strength of the records of Lhuyd and Brewer, but it was in fact John Ray who first recorded the plant in Anglesey during his tour through North Wales in 1662. There have been no subsequent records for this plant from Anglesey.

Despite the fact that the mistletoe (*Viscum album*) was not actually seen growing wild on the island, Davies nevertheless decided to include it in his flora in the belief that the Druids, whose stronghold was Anglesey, held the plant in very high esteem and made extensive use of it in their ceremonies and as a medicine. The mistletoe is normally found growing on apple trees, but the Druids believed that if it was found growing on oak then it was especially sacred. Davies adds. 'I have not seen this plant, but we can scarcely suppose that the Druids had fixed upon, as a favourite residence, a spot that did not produce this highly venerated plant; add to this that there is a place in the parish of Llangeinwen which is supposed to take its name from it.'

The juniper is listed on the strength of the fact that a place bears the Welsh name for Juniper. 'I venture this as once an inhabitant, from the name of a place, Cefn y Ferywen, the Juniper Bank, in the parish of Llanidan.' In 1978 the dwarf juniper (*Juniperis communis subsp. alpina*) was found growing on sea cliffs near Holyhead and the record appears in R.H. Roberts' *'The Flowering Plants and Ferns of Anglesey'* (1982).

Griffith (1894/5) and Roberts (1982) both record the Scots pine (*Pinus sylvestris*) from Anglesey in their respective floras as being 'frequent in old plantations'. Davies, however, does not include this species on the same grounds, but only on evidence which proves that the tree did at one time grow on the island. He states that the timber remains dug up with peat, and the tree stumps that were found while deepening the outlet of Llyn Llwydiarth near Pentraeth proved to be that of Scots pine, 'as the sylvestris is the only species of Pinus indigenous in Britain'.

The rusty-back fern (*Ceterach officinarum*) according to Davies, was being gathered from caves on Holyhead mountain and used for bait in rock-cod-fishing, and as a result its numbers had been greatly reduced.

The *Welsh Botanology* includes a wealth of Welsh plant names which had either been collected locally from the eldest inhabitants and the writings of William Morris and others, or coined by the author. We are indebted to Hugh Davies for collating and publishing these old 'British' names, as he calls them, and they have formed the basis from which modern Welsh plant name collectors have built upon.

One of the Welsh plant names of the dwarf elder (*Sambucus ebulus*) is given as 'Gwaed y gwyr' (Blood of the warrior), as is tutsan, (*Hypericum androsaemum*), but Davies in a footnote favours the latter as being the most worthy. ' . . . that if the yellow flowering tops are bruised between the fingers, they will immediately communicate a deep crimson stain. The Ebulus [elder] claims it on the strength of a fabulous tale, that the plant originally sprung from the blood of the Danes, who were slain in Britain, whence it has also obtained the English name Dane-wort.'

Davies names two local botanists whose records he includes in his *Welsh Botanology*. The Reverend Evan Lloyd found meadow clary (*Salvia pratensis*) on Cwirt Farm in the parish of Llangeinwen, but Griffith (1894/5) dismisses this as an error for wild clary (*Salvia verbenaca*) which he found near Penmon Priory, as did Davies (1813). In Griffith's opinion the plant specimens labelled '*Salvia pratensis*' in Davies' Herbarium was in fact '*Salvia verbenaca*'. There have been no recent records of either of these plants from Anglesey. Lloyd can also be credited with the first discovery in the county of the meadow saxifrage (*Saxifraga granulata*) which he found on the sandy pastures of Rhuddgaer Farm near Llangeinwen. Davies confirms the find by adding that he, later, had found the plant in abundance at the same site; recent accounts (Roberts 1982) show that it still flourishes in various sites at the southern corner of the island.

The common wintergreen (*Pyrola minor*) is recorded for Anglesey by Davies on the testimony of William Morris of Holyhead, who was mentioned earlier as having prepared a list of plants of the island in a manuscript which later came to be in the possession of Davies. Morris found the plant in Lligwy Wood, (circa 1750) but no record of it has been noted since that time. In 1955 R.H. Roberts of Bangor found the round-leaved wintergreen (*Pyrola rotundifolia*), for the first time in Anglesey in Newborough Warren, and since that time the plant has been seen in other parts of the island.

It seems hardly credible that even in those far off days plants could suffer due to industrial pollution. Davies however, points out that the purple melic-grass (*Melica caerulea*) had withstood the sulpherous fumes of the copperworks at Amlwch, 'where every other vegetable, within a certain distance, even the crustaceous lichens, have been destroyed'. This grass is known today as *Molinia caurulea*, purple moor-grass.

The exploitation of the earth's natural resources was well under way during Davies' lifetime, and experiments in land improvement and reclamation were also imminent. It would appear that he was not as keen as his contemporary, John Wynne Griffith of Garn, on modernising farming methods and the utilization of land. Davies possessed a very intimate and thorough knowledge of his native island, and whilst out on his botanical rambles he would inquire into the past use of a piece of land when he felt an explanation was necessary as to the appearance of a plant that he had not previously seen there; plants that would today be referred to as 'aliens'. The following comment is added to his record of thorn-apple (*Datura stramonium*). 'This plant was produced abundantly on cutting up a piece of old ground in the demesne of Maes y Porth; [Dwyran] it is known that this land has undergone no process in agriculture within a century, prior to this'. At a time when conservation as we know it was unheard of, Davies was noticing the changes that were taking place around him, and this becomes clear in another of his comments in his book which he inserts while dealing with the smooth-stalked sedge (*Carex laevigata*). 'This species I discovered many years ago on Ty fry demesne; it has been totally destroyed in a meadow which once abounded with it; but is still found on the side of a deep glen, which lies about south of the mansion, where it is likely to bid defiance to the ruthless hand of improvement, both imaginary and real.' These are the words of a man who had forseen the rape of the Industrial and Agricultural Revolutions and the effect it was bound to have on the habitats of the plants he had studied during his lifetime.

Davies was quick to point out any errors he found in the work of other writers on natural history, but he would always explain his objections and disagreements in his own particular style. He disagrees with Edward Lhuyd on the Welsh name of the darnel grass (*Lolium temulentum*), which, according to Davies is given as 'Ller' in the *Archeologia Britannica*. The full name of 'Pawr-wellt Ller' is given in *Welsh Botanology* for the rye brome grass (*Bromus secalinus*) as it has 'none of the noxious qualities of the other'. The attention given by Davies to finding the correct Welsh plant names and their uses becomes evident in his note on the sea plantain (*Plantago maritima*) where nearly a whole page is dedicated to the agricultural value of the plant. The author points out how names like 'llys y defaid', (the sheep's vegetable), 'sampier y ddafad' (the sheep's samphire) and 'bara can y defaid' (the sheep's favourite morsel) proves that it was regarded as an important grazing plant, and also as a cure to common ailments in cattle. In the same note Davies mentions an error in Withering's *Arrangement of British Plants* (1796) where the rock samphire (*Crithmum maritimum*) is credited with the medicinal qualities which should have been attributed to the sea plantain (*Plantago maritima*). Withering in a footnote (vol.2, page 295) also gives the following uses. 'Poor people on the sea coast eat it as a pot-herb, and gather it for sale, it being much used as a pickle. — Sheep and cows eagerly feed, and are said to grow fat, upon it.'

The second part of *Welsh Botanology* was, to quote the full title, 'an Alphabetical Catalogue of the Welsh names of Vegetables rendered into Latin and English with some account of the qualities, economical or medicinal, of the most remarkable.'

The plants are listed in alphabetical order; first the Welsh name, followed by the scientific and English names. The introduction, and the details for preparing the medicinal cures, are written in Welsh, and this part of the book was intended as a Herbal which would be advantageous to families who lived many miles from the nearest doctor in scattered farms or remote villages. In his introduction Hugh Davies pays tribute to Dr John Davies of Mallwyd (c.1567-1644) Meirionnydd, who in his Welsh-Latin Dictionary published up to 1,000 Welsh plant names, and also to the manuscripts of 'Meddygon

WELSH BOTANOLOGY;

PART THE FIRST.

A

SYSTEMATIC CATALOGUE

OF THE

NATIVE PLANTS

OF THE

ISLE OF ANGLESEY,

IN

LATIN, ENGLISH, AND WELSH;

WITH THE HABITATS OF THE RARER SPECIES, AND A FEW OBSERVATIONS.

TO WHICH IS ADDED,

AN APPENDIX,

CONSISTING OF

THOSE GENERA, IN THE THREE FIRST VOLUMES OF FLORA BRITANNICA,
WHICH ARE NOT OF SPONTANEOUS GROWTH IN ANGLESEY,
RENDERED LIKEWISE INTO WELSH.

BY HUGH DAVIES, F.L.S.

Nomina si nescis, perit et cognitio rerum.
Phil. Bot.

LONDON:

PRINTED, FOR THE AUTHOR,
BY W. MARCHANT, INGRAM-COURT, FENCHURCH-STREET; AND SOLD BY
E. WILLIAMS, NO. 11, STRAND; AND T. POOLE, CHESTER.

1813.

Myddfai', the well known mediaeval physicians, named after the village of Myddfai in Carmarthenshire. It may be interesting to note that Dr John Davies' list of Welsh plant names was copied from the manuscripts of Thomas Wiliems (1545/6-1622) of Trefriw, (mentioned previously) priest, scribe, lexicographer and physician who compiled a Latin-Welsh Dictionary which was never published. In effect the lineage of some of the Welsh plant names can be derived from Salesbury's Herbal to the works of Thomas Wiliems, to the *Botanologium* of the *Dictionarum Duplex* of John Davies (1632) up to the time of William Morris, accumulating steadily in the course of time.

The *Welsh Botanology* is both a county flora and a family Herbal. It is the first complete catalogue of plants listed of any county in Wales, and perhaps, even more important to its author, it provided him with an opportunity to publish the vast collection of Welsh plant names that he had so diligently amassed during his lifetime.

Conflicting Views of Snowdonia

Conrad Gesner, a 16th century Zurich naturalist made an early ascent of Pilatus in the Bernese Alps, and could well be the first botanical mountaineer. His feelings towards mountains was unique for his period. He climbed mountains 'for the delight of the mind and the proper exercise of the body'. The following is a translated passage from one of his letters.

'Think of the moment in which are concentrated for the climber such things as these: the relaxation after arduous toil, the cool refreshment that succeeds excessive heat, the quenching of a burning thirst, the satisfying of a keener appetite than that of every day; add to all this a mind at peace with all the world, pleasantly concious of the presence and the talk of friends, and you cannot fail to see that in such a moment the height of bliss is reached.'

It is often said that the early travellers who visited Snowdonia did not appreciate the wild grandeur of the mountainous scenery and were more attracted to the historical antiquities found in towns and cities rather than the natural delights of the countryside. This however was not always the case, and Thomas Johnson, the London apothecary mentioned earlier, certainly had an eye for natural views and a high opinion of the inhabitants of North Wales. Johnson had some unique theories regarding the origins of the Welsh nation, and he explains these theories in the foreword of his book *Mercurii Botanici Pars Altera* (1641) which was translated into English under the title *The Itinerary of a Botanist* in 1908. According to Johnson the Welsh people were the remnants of a noble British race who inhabited the south-eastern corner of England prior to the Roman occupation, who had to flee their lands during the invasion and found refuge in the mountains of Wales where they settled. 'And this part of the island, up to the present day, produced men famous in war, and in the pursuits of peace. Nor will you anywhere easily find men who are well-born, magnanimous, upright, loyal and hospitable, and if true nobility derives its origin from manliness, it must be confessed that this nation is truly noble.' To Johnson, the Welsh language is the 'language of ancient Britain', and he proved that he was aware that it was still the language of the people by bringing along Edward Morgan to act as interpreter.

Johnson, being a naturalist, appreciated picturesque scenery, and differed from other early visitors by actually enjoying the views of the mountains from the grounds of Glynllifon where he stayed; 'on the other side our British Alps . . . rear themselves up, so that wheresoever you go there is something worth seeing.'

The main purpose of Johnson's visit was to collect rare and interesting plants, but his writings leave us in little doubt that the journey in itself also gave him pleasure.

Most of the early travellers were botanists, and some of them were so preoccupied with their subject that it made them quite oblivious both to the surrounding scenery and to the perils of the localities they visited. Samuel Brewer was just such a botanist. He dismissed his guide on Clogwyn Du'r Arddu because he refused to follow him up the rocks, and on Anglesey he explored the swampy bogs of Cors Llechylched ' . . . for a mile together in water above our knees, and the earth shaking under us'. Brewer's obsession with his plant hunting was paramount, and although the weather is sometimes referred to in his diary, he makes no mention of the scenery. One gets the impression that he would have been just as happy conducting his searches inside an enormous greenhouse, or a laboratory, and that he most probably would never have noticed the difference.

Some of the comments that the early scientists made regarding mountains were quite remarkable, as the following passage from an early edition of Camden's *Britannia* testifies. 'On the interior parts nature had reared groupes of mountains as if she meant her to bind the island fast to the bowels of the earth.'

Another early traveller who found mountain scenery aesthetically pleasing was Lord George Lyttleton, and unlike Thomas Johnson, he was a politician and not a naturalist. Lord Lyttleton's itinerary to North Wales in 1756 however differed from those of his contemporaries in as much as he chose to climb Moel Hebog and not Snowdon, and this he did by a western route as opposed to the more normally used Beddgelert track. 'The hill we stood upon,' he wrote, 'was perfectly clear, the way we came up a pretty easy ascent; but before us was a precipice of many hundred yards, and below, a vale, which, though not cultivated, has much savage beauty.' He came to North Wales to prepare himself for an election campaign, 'so that I may, by this ramble, preserve a stock of health that may last the winter, and carry me through my parliamentary campaign.'

Turning to Samuel Johnson we find that he was certainly no mountaineer; in fact he seemed to be quite unaccustomed to any excessive bodily exertion and his walk up to Dolbadarn Castle near Llanberis left him quite breathless. The natural beauties of Snowdonia made little impression on him, compared to that of the Lake District of which he wrote, 'Ilam excels Dovedale by the extent of its prospects, the awfulness of its shades, the horrors of its precipices, the verdure of its hollows, and the loftiness of its rocks. The ideas which it forces upon the mind are, the sublime, the dreadful, and the vast. Above is inaccessible altitude, is horrible profundity. Its grandeur is tempered with softness; the walker congratulates his own arrival at the place, and is greaved to think he must ever leave it. As he looks up to the rocks, his thoughts are elevated; as he turns his eyes on the vallies, he is composed and soothed . . . He that mounts the precipices wonder how he came thither, and doubts how he shall return. His walk is an adventure, and his departure an escape. He has not the tranquillity, but the horrors, of solitude; a kind of turbulent pleasure, between fright and admiration.'

It was probably the fertile greenery and gentle beauty of the Lake District that motivated Johnson to write these words, the craggy wild greyness of Snowdonia failing to induce any comment from him as did his beloved English hills. First impressions usually count with mountaineers. The same could be said of Dr Johnson, who favoured the 'pretty' as opposed to the 'awe inspiring'.

There was a marked difference in the attitude of the travellers who visited Wales from the last quarter of the 18th century onwards, and during that period fifty individual tours through Wales were published. Before this time some of the comments made by tourists on Wales and the Welsh were quite offensive. In 1670 Charles Cotton wrote of 'hills and valleys uncouth and uneven' where he was forced to crawl on all fours in the company of a guide who had, 'a voice like a cricket, a look like a rat: The brain of a goose and the heart of a cat'. The Welsh language suffered similar abuse. 'Their native gibberish is usually prattled throughout the whole of Taphydom except in the market towns, whose inhabitants being a little raised do begin to despise it. 'Tis usually cashiered out of gentlemen's houses, there being scarcely to be heard even one single Welsh Tom (sic) in many families so that (if the stars prove lucky) there may be some glimmering hopes that the British language may be quite extinct and may be English'd out of Wales.' These were quite different comments to those made by Thomas Johnson the apothecary earlier that century.

However when Joseph Craddock published his *Letters from Snowdon* in 1770, he wrote passionately and with an enthusiasm for scenery; a fashion which came to be adopted by most of the contemporary authors of the Welsh 'tours'. Craddock stayed in Snowdonia as the guest of the curate of one of the parishes, the name of which is not given, but from its description and proximity to Llyn Cwellyn, could have been Beddgelert or Betws Garmon. The curate was also his guide to Snowdon, which they ascended from a 'hut' near Llyn Cwellyn; the views completely overwhelmed Craddock, as did his stay among the hills. 'O my friend,' he wrote, 'why should we return to the busy haunt of men? why were we doomed to drag an existence in populous cities and the crowded forum! O that it had been our lot to live among these mountains, unenvied and unknown.' Craddock also enjoyed the company of the local inhabitants, and he took the trouble to learn a few Welsh words, which, together with a few coins given in gratuity, helped him to gain their trust. While spending the evening in a 'small thatched hut' prior to their ascent of Snowdon, 'a poor blind harper' was sent for and a number of 'blooming country girls' entertained them with singing and dancing. Craddock enjoyed the music. 'There is something very plaintive and affecting in the Welsh music, and the manner of their singing symphonious and responsive to the notes of the harp, renders it exceeding melodious.' His comments on Welsh poetry however, were quite the opposite, and here again we have that old aloof imperialistic attitude influencing his opinions. 'The poets, or such as pretend to be such, arrogate to themselves a most unwarrantable poetical licence of coining words, for the sake of sound; and this they will seldom scruple to do, whenever they want a word for rhyme. Hence the greatest part of their poetry, is nothing more than melodious nonsense, a perfect jargon of harmonious sounds. And when translated, scarce reducible to common sense.' Craddock formed these opinions of Welsh poetry during his short stay in Snowdonia, and sadly he failed to understand or appreciate the rule that permits a bard to coin words for use in rhyme. When he asked for the meaning of a certain word he was given the translation literally, which did not always make sense, and what he failed to understand he chose to ridicule. His comments on the Welsh language also illustrate a self-opinionated character, with no previous knowledge of the country. He sees the Welsh as a nation which had benefited but little from the improvements of the civilized world, and one gets the impression that his judgements, although seen through an imperialistic eye, are at the same time compassionate.

In conclusion, perhaps it is Arthur Aikin, who toured North Wales during the summer of 1796, in the company of two friends who best sums up this issue. ' . . . but the requisite knowledge of a sufficient number of circumstances from which to deduce a national character is not to be acquired without long residence and much intercourse with the inhabitants.'

Arthur Aikin (1773-1854), who was a chemist and interested mainly in minerology, also made botanical observations and contributed a list of Shropshire plants to Turner and Dillwyn's *Botanist's Guide* published in 1805. He entered Snowdonia through the pass of Aberglaslyn recording such plants as white water-lily (*Nymphaea alba*), royal fern (*Osmunda regalis*), bog-myrtle (*Myrica gale*) and beaked tasselweed (*Ruppia maritima*) on the way. Aikin passed this way before Madocks' embankment was built across Traeth Mawr and at a time when the sea reached up to Aberglaslyn, and he found the beaked tasselweed 'in the pools and ditches of the marshes covered by the tide . . . the fruit-stalks are formed by an elastic spiral line, contracting or elongating itself according to the depth of the water.' Aikin ascended Snowdon from Llyn Cwellyn, along the Snowdon Ranger path which in his day started near Bron y Fedw, a hill farm which has a long history with the old Snowdon guides. Aikin failed to hire the services of a guide because it was a Sunday, but nevertheless took advantage of the fine weather and set out with his colleagues for the summit. He makes no record of the plants he saw, but dismisses them as being the same as he found on Cadair Idris, which suggests that he did not visit the localities of the rarities due to the absence of a local guide. His comments are on the whole to do with the geology of the area, and he was also impressed by the black cattle and the sheep that were left unattended to graze on the lower parts of the mountain. The views, as is often the case with the writers of the 'tours', are also described in fine prose but without the lengthy over-dramatic style of most of the others. As a scientist he was interested in the varying temperatures recorded on the summit in comparison with that of the valleys, and he must have made a night ascent in 1795 for he was on the summit of Snowdon watching the sunrise on 5 July where he states the temperature to be 34°F and 48°F at the same place at 1 o'clock in the afternoon. The temperature recorded for him at Beddgelert at 7 o'clock on the same morning was 62°F. While on the summit during his 1796 journey he saw three ring ouzels 'amid the thickness of the clouds' and goes on to say that the eagle was also an occasional visitor to the 'loftiest crags'. On the day after the Snowdon trip Aikin and his friends set out from Beddgelert bound for Llanrwst; a walk of about 20 miles which they took amid showers of heavy rain. The unusually wet weather of that summer had all but destroyed the hay crop noted while passing the enclosures of land near Llyn Dinas and the hill farmers had taken the precaution of placing slabs of stone on top of each stack to keep them from being washed into the lake with the mountain torrents. Aikin describes the enclosed land around Llyn Dinas as being better that average, as 'mosses, orchides, and asphodels, with a small proportion of grass which was mown to serve for the winter provision of the cattle and sheep.' On arriving at the head of Llyn Dinas they continued along the road towards Llyn Gwynant, but failed to ford the river due to the ferocious rush of water, so they struck a narrow footpath which eventually brought them to the head of Llyn Gwynant, after having 'forced their way through a steep swampy wood'. The 'road' up to Bwlch Ehediad from Llyn Gwynant is described as 'a continued series of rude broken steps, very narrow and winding, ascending the steep face of a craggy mountain that overlooks the lake, without any parapet wall, or the slightest barrier, in places where the descent is all but perpendicular.' After reaching the top of the 'Bwlch' they crossed the wide boggy tract in torrential rain, and on descending the other side they could make out the form of Dolwyddelan Castle through the clouds. On arriving at Dolwyddelan they managed, with some difficulty arising from language problems, to obtain refreshments before continuing their journey to Llanrwst in the Conwy valley. Aikin records that the 'neat farmhouses and gentlemen's seats give an air of plenty and civilization to this valley. Here we found no difficulty in inquiring our road, for we have invariably found the English language understood in the fertile and populous parts'.

Aikin, like Craddock before him, was much impressed with the singing of harmonious melodies to the accompaniment of the Welsh harp; a custom popular in the inns and public places in North Wales. J. Lloyd Williams,

(1854-1945), botanist and musician, writing of his childhood days in Llanrwst during the 1860s recalls how his father used to sing old Welsh ballads to the accompaniment of the harp around the inns of the town.

Observations concerning the lead mines at Gwydir and the copper mines of Llanberis take up most of the chapter which records the journey from Llanrwst to Caernarfon, and is of great interest to students of Minerology. On enquiring after lodgings at Capel Curig they found the houses deserted and the inhabitants gone to Llanrwst Fair, so they continued their journey in the direction of Llanberis, but missed the junction of the horse track at Pen y gwryd and subsequently found themselves approaching Llyn Gwynant. In order to avoid retracing their steps the party then decided to climb directly from the hollow of Cwm Dyli and managed to gain the Llanberis track at the top of the pass. Their appetites were soon satisfied at a 'hovel of an inn' at Llanberis, (now Nant Peris) and the list of plants seen *en route* though small in number, are nevertheless interesting. Near Capel Curig they saw venus'-looking-glass (*Legousia hybrida*); a plant of arable fields in South East England, and not recorded since from Snowdonia. The tiny filmy fern (*Hymenophyllum*) was noted as being collected 'near Llanberis', but it is impossible to say if it was either the *Hymenophyllum wilsonii*, or the *Hymenophyllum tunbrigense*, as the two British species were not distinguished until after Aikin's day. Parsley fern (*Cryptogramma crispa*) was and still is a common fern in Snowdonia, as is also the lemon-scented fern (*Oreopteris limbosperma*).

The 'Classic Tours'

Thomas Pennant (1726-1798) naturalist and antiquary had according to Samuel Johnson, 'greater variety of inquiry than almost any man, and has told us more than perhaps one in ten thousand could have done in the time he took. He has not said what he was to tell, so you cannot find fault with him for what he has not told.' Pennant's much acclaimed *Tours in Wales* are considered accurate and informative sources of information and are frequently consulted by historians. He was not, by his own admission, a botanist, but he nevertheless noted a number of plants while on his mountain excursions, and is credited with the first record for Caernarfonshire of the alpine meadow-grass (*Poa alpina*) which he saw while ascending Snowdon under the guidance of Hugh Shone. They began their ascent from Llanberis and after the climb past Ceunant Mawr, the much visited Llanberis waterfall, they crossed the lower meadows of Cwmbrwynog and joined the Snowdon Ranger track after crossing Bwlch Maesgwm and descending a short distance on the Betws Garmon side. The plants mentioned during this trip are mainly grasses and rushes and Pennant explains the term 'gwair y rhosydd', as being the local term for a mixture of rushes, sedges and grasses which are still the dominant plants on the lower moorland slopes of Snowdonia. Literally translated 'gwair y rhosydd' means moorland grasses. Like most of the other travellers he notes

Thomas Pennant (1726-1798)

the sheep and cattle grazing high on the mountain during the summer months and also the 'hafodtai', or summer dwellings, where the hill farmers stay to be nearer their stock before herding them back to the 'hendre', or winter dwelling in early autumn; Pennant compares this custom to that practised by the farmers in the Swiss Alps and their *'sennes'*. These summer dairy houses are described as consisting 'of a long low room with a hole at one end, to let out the smoke from the fire which is made beneath,' where the family lived in spartan style using stones for stools and hay for beds. Their homespun cloths were dyed using lichen gathered off the mountain rocks; the lichen was named by Pennant as *'Lichen omphaloides'*, and William Withering (1796) notes the following uses of the plant as a dye: 'It dyes wool of a brown reddish colour, or a dull but durable crimson or purple, paler but more lasting than that of Orchal. It is prepared by the country people in Ireland by steeping it in stale urine, adding a little salt to it, and making it up into balls with lime. Wool dyed with it and then dipped in the blue vat becomes of a beautiful purple. With rotten oak it makes a good dark brown frize. Wool dyed with red wood, or sanders, and afterwards in corker, becomes of a dark reddish brown.' The substance was also used to check the bleeding from a wound, and it was known by the common names, cork, corker, arcell, and according to Pennant, as 'cenn du y Cerrig' in Welsh.

Pennant climbed the Glyder from 'Pont y gwryd', where the servants were directed to proceed to Llanberis with the horses, and after reaching the summit of Glyder Fach he descended via the Gribin ridge to Cwm Bochlwyd and on to Nant Ffrancon. His trip to Cwm Idwal, Glyder Fawr, Llyn y Cŵn and down to Llanberis was undertaken on another day, and he describes the way as passing 'beneath that vast precipice Castell y Geifr, or The Castle of the Goats'. The Devil's Kitchen, or Twll Du, is described as 'a stupendous *roche fendue* and 'Klogwyn Du Ymhen y Glyder' is as 'dreadful a precipice as any in Snowdonia'. Pennant was aware that this area was much frequented by botanists, and names the alpine saxifrage (*Saxifraga nivalis*), Snowdon lily (*Lloydia serotina*), and *'Lichen islandicus'* (*Cetraria islandica*), as being among the plants found here, but does not say whether or not he saw them there himself. The *'Lichen islandicus'* (*Cetraria islandica*) was used by the people of Iceland and is thus described by Pennant. 'A decoction of the fresh leaves in water serves them in the spring as a powerful cathartic; and yet, when dried, changes its quality, and, if grinded to powder, is a common food, either made into bread, or boiled with milk, or water.' It was also used as a cure for coughs and consumption. Llyn y Cŵn is also noted by Pennant as being a spot worthy of a visit by botanists. The lake he declares to be devoid of any fish, and questions the claim made by Giraldus in his *Itinerary through Wales* in 1188, who said that the lake yielded trout, perch, and eels, all of which were wanting a left eye. It must be noted that Giraldus does not actually name Llyn y Cŵn as being the lake connected with the folk-tale of the one-eyed fish, and Pennant most probably saw the reference to it in Gibson's edition of Camden's *Britannia* (1722) which states: 'The lake wherein he [Giraldus] tells us there's a wandering island, is a small Pond, call'd Lhyn y Dywarchen (i.e. *Lacus cespitis,*) from a little green moveable patch, which is all the occasion of the Fable of the wandering Island; but whence that other of monocular Fish (which he says were found also at two places in Scotland) took beginning, I have nothing to say, but that it is credibly reported that Trouts having only one eye are sometimes taken at Lhyn ykwn near Lhan Berys.' Edward Lhuyd, who contributed substantial additions to this edition of *Britannia*, probably had the folk-tale related to him during one of his visits to Snowdonia as also did Giraldus five hundred years before him.

The plants recorded from in and around the lake are water lobelia (*Lobelia dortmanna*) awlwort (*Subularia aquatica*) and quillwort (*Isoetes lacustris*). It was here also that he made the first record of the three-flowered rush (*Juncus triglumis*), a notable 'find' for a man who once stated of himself, 'botany is not within my province'. He also notes the alpine hawkweed (*Hieracium holosericeum*) from the same area and it is interesting that the first record of this plant is credited to Sir Joseph Banks who with the Reverend John Lightfoot undertook a botanical tour of Wales in 1773, which was the same year that Pennant did his first tour.

Thomas Pennant came from Downing in Flintshire, and he was proud of his Welshness, a factor which is clearly illustrated in his writing, 'we sustained our independency . . . against the power of a kingdom more than twelve times larger than Wales', he wrote, 'and at length had the glory of falling, when a divided country, beneath the arms of the most wise and warlike of the English monarchs'.

Pennant's travels to North Wales were undertaken in 1773 and 1776 accompanied by Moses Griffith, the celebrated artist from Bryncroes, Lleyn, who illustrated the published works, including the Scottish tours, and also the author's books on natural history which contain a large number of illustrations of animals, birds and fishes.

Pennant enjoyed his mountain walks and favoured traversing the hills and returning by a different route to that which was used to ascend. It will be remembered that the guide Hugh Shone led Pennant up Snowdon by the Snowdon Ranger, which they had reached via Bwlch Maesgwm from Cwm-brwynog, and then came down the pony track, which is known as the Llanberis path today. Hugh Shone according to Pennant was 'a most able conductor' and this testimonial would have been considered useful by the guide and kept for future reference.

The poet William Sotheby was also pleased with his guide, and in his book entitled *A Tour Thro' Parts of North and South Wales, Sonnets Odes and other*

Poems . . . ' (1794) gives the following account.

'Thee, Snowdon! King of Cambrian mountains hail!
With many a lengthened pause my lingering feet
Follow the experienced guide; a veteran maimed
With glorious wounds, that late on Calpe's height
Bled in his country's cause; though time has marked
With graceful touch his silver hair, yet health,
The child of temperance, has fixed the rose
Of youth upon his cheek; keen beams his eye
Beneath his hoary brow, and firm his foot
Springs on the steepness of the rough ascent.
Proud of his native land the veteran points
To every mountain, wood and winding stream,
That by tradition sacred made records
His great forefathers' deeds: for not derived
Of simple lineage the brave warrior boasts
Hereditary blood of British Chiefs.'

The anonymous guide, a soldier wounded on active duty in Gibraltar, knew well his native mountains and took delight in narrating to his charge the legends and folklore related to them. How sad that the poet did not pass on to us the name of this wounded 'warrior' so that he could, together with the sonnet, achieve immortality.

There is further evidence of wounded ex-servicemen acting as guides in North Wales. In 1794 Robert Clutterbuck left Dolgellau under the guidance of an old sailor who had lost an arm in the service of his country, and two years later Sir Christopher Sykes writes: 'Our guide Henry Roberts was an old soldier wanting an arm aged 67. His mother living aged 88, his father died 7 years ago, aged 87. They had been married 67 years and lived about two miles up the mountain. He [Henry Roberts] now keeps a turnpike gate at Dolgellau.'

In addition to the highland guides who operated in the mountain areas there were also the lowland guides who were hired by travellers to lead them across the remote and often trackless terrain between towns and villages. One such tract of land which led many a traveller astray was that which lay between Harlech and Penmorfa, and prior to the completion of the embankment across the mouth of the river Glaslyn in 1811 guides were employed to cross the notoriously treacherous sands of Traeth Mawr and Traeth Bach if the tide was out.

Henry Penruddocke Wyndham toured Wales and Monmouthshire in 1774 and 1777 and his comments on the guides of this area are not very complimentary. 'In order to avoid the goat track of our morning ride,' he writes, 'we returned over the sands of the Traeth Bychan, which are only passable at low water. It is remarkable, that we had hitherto never deviated from the true line of our route, when alone; and that we seldom failed of doing it when we employed a guide.' Wyndham's guide from Tan y Bwlch lost his way twice while leading the party to and from Harlech, 'and we were obliged to have guide upon guide, before we ventured to cross the sands, which are by no means difficult when known, but which, from their shifting and quickness, are intricate and dangerous to strangers.' He goes on to accuse Welsh guides of blundering through the country, preferring to make a mistake rather than stop to ask the way, which would give away their lack of knowledge; 'till he himself is really alarmed, at which time he becomes more terrified, than those he pretends to conduct.' Wyndham's Harlech guide refused to admit his mistakes until the party were led to the verge of a steep cliff down which it was impossible to descend. This was the fourth incompetent guide whom Wyndham had the misfortune to hire during his Welsh tour, and this induced him to use horse drawn carriages on his second journey. He nevertheless found it necessary to revert to guides to attend to the horses whenever they wanted to travel beyond the range of the coaches and even this caused problems . . . 'and it would appear incredible, if I was to repeat, how, consequently, we were almost daily bewildered between stage and stage.'

The guides who led travellers across the treacherous sands of Traeth Mawr and Traeth Bach were operational until 1820. Traeth Bach was crossed at the estuary of the river Dwyryd by a route connecting Talsarnau and Penrhyndeudraeth, while Traeth Mawr, the Glaslyn estuary, was undertaken from either Penrhyndeudraeth or Llanfrothen across to Penmorfa. John Lloyd, or Sion Llwyd, who kept an inn called 'Ceunant' at Llanfrothen during the 1740s served as guide during this time, and his son, of the same name, took over from him until 1820. Another of the known guides from this district was William Jones of Abergafran, Penrhyndeudraeth who died in 1830. There are several entries in parish burial registers which testify to the number of those unfamiliar with the area who ventured alone onto the sands and were drowned. Wiser travellers would look for an ash tree which once stood close to the edge of the sands near Rhos Penrhyndeudraeth. This tree bore a sign in the shape of a white horse on which was displayed the words 'Guide for the Sands'.

Bron y Fedw, 'The Guide's House'

Several references are made by travellers during the latter part of the 18th century to the 'guide's house near Llyn Cwellyn', as being the starting point of the ascent of Snowdon. This was Bron y Fedw in Betws Garmon, and traces of the old farmhouse can still be seen by the side of the stream above the present Bron y Fedw Isaf, close to the path connecting Nant y Betws and Llanberis. This is the path which can also be used to reach the summit of Snowdon by turning off and following the Snowdon Ranger path at the point where the two paths cross higher up on the hillside.

An old manuscript written in 1775 refers to climbing Snowdon from 'Bronfedow the Shepherd's House' but he met his guide on his arrival at Caernarfon. It is not clear if he came there to meet him or if the guide was actually from the town. The Reverend J. Poole and Charles Joseph Harford also had difficulties finding 'Griffiths the guide a little beyond Betws Garmon'. When the house was eventually found it was described as 'a cottage on the side of the hill about two fields out of the road on the left hand'. Ellis Griffith the guide was busy attending to the chores around the farm and was barefooted when the visitors arrived; on agreeing to their proposals he soon put on stockings and shoes and his best coat, and began the ascent of Snowdon at 12.35 p.m. One of the duties expected of a guide was to collect plants for the visitors and this Ellis Griffith did: 'Our guide had gatherd most of the Alpine plants for which he had ventured on the rocks and cliffs with the intrepidity of the goats'.

Other tourists have noted Ellis Griffith's goat-like agility and these talents were often put to more practical uses than just plant collecting. A certain Mrs Griffiths and Miss Bell visited North Wales during the 1790s and whilst journeying from Caernarfon to Tan y Bwlch they ascended Snowdon from Bron y Fedw under the guidance of Ellis Griffith. It was a blustery day; the strong wind blew the hats, handkerchiefs and in one instance, the nightcap of one of the ladies over the cliff tops, 'and our guide skipped like a goat to the very verge of the precipice to recover them'. In the course of the conversation which ensued the grateful tourists record that Ellis Griffith at this time was paying the Vaynol Estate an annual rent of £28 for his farm and kept nineteen milking cows. Five people resided at the farm, husband and wife, a son and two daughters and they 'lived almost intirely on the produce of the dairy as their beverage was nothing but milk and whey'.

During the summer of 1794 the author of another 'Tour' called upon the services of Ellis Griffith. He was a young Cambridge graduate of 23 years of age called Joseph Hucks, who together with Samuel Taylor Coleridge the poet and two others arrived in Beddgelert by the Caernarfon road. Hucks and Coleridge had begun their tour by entering Wales from Gloucester, continued northwards to Welshpool, Bala, Wrexham, Denbigh and Holywell before turning westward, joining up with two Cambridge students on the way, and followed the coast to Caernarfon, visiting Anglesey on the way. At 11 o'clock on a stormy night the party set out from Beddgelert to look for the guide's house which they had learned was a distance of five miles from the village. Hucks notes that 'Bethkelert' was the usual place from which the tourists made their ascent of Snowdon; but they became quite lost in the dark on the way to Betws Garmon. They eventually saw a faint light on the hillside above the road, and directing their steps in this direction they came to a 'small hut' where they found that the family had retired for the night. It was some time before an elderly man appeared at the door, and like most of the natives of Snowdonia during this period he neither spoke nor understood the English language. After some difficulty the party succeeded in making themselves understood, and on hearing the words 'Ellis Griffith' and 'Snowdon' frequently repeated, the old man agreed to lead them to the house of the Snowdon guide. After a half hour's walk they arrived at another cottage to which they were admitted by a young man of about seventeen years of age who turned out to be the man they were looking for. The guide firmly advised against any attempt at climbing Snowdon that night, so the party decided to wait until morning in the hope that the weather would be improved by then. Hucks spent the night reading an old Welsh dictionary by rush-light while his friends lay on the benches either side of the open fireplace, from which the dying embers of the peat fire gave comfort against the sounds of wind and rain and the gushing torrents of the cataract close by.

Hucks records awakening the household at 4.00 a.m. the following morning; the weather not being particularly improved the other members however decided to attempt the excursion while Hucks returned to the inn at Beddgelert to wait for the others who did not arrive until 4 in the afternoon. The ascent of Snowdon was undertaken mainly for the purpose of finding plants rather than for the view from the top as Hucks had stated earlier that 'One of my companions was a very skilful botanist, and his botanical furor induced him at all times to despise danger and difficulty, when in pursuit of a favourite plant . . . ' The party seems to have suffered similarly at the hands of the 'skilful botanist' during their stay at Caernarfon when he expressed a desire to cross the Straits to Anglesey in order to see a rare plant. Soon after coming off the ferry at Abermenai it began to rain very hard, so they made their way back again as it began to grow dark. The two-mile crossing was very rough and the rain, plus the spray of sea-water thoroughly soaked them.

There is no evidence as to which member of the party was the botanist; the two Cambridge students who accompanied Coleridge and Hucks, joining them at Conwy, were John Brooke (1773-1821) and Thomas Berdmore and neither one are known to have been botanists.

Ellis Griffith was baptized on 1 January 1778, and on 19 October 1804 at Beddgelert married Ann Evans, the daughter of Dafydd Evan of Talymignedd Farm in the Nantlle valley. They had three children, Ellis, Ann and Jane. The couple went to live at the present Bron y Fedw Uchaf soon after the wedding; this farmhouse became the home of the local Methodist Sunday Schools until a chapel was built in 1825. Ellis Griffith died on 26 August 1810 aged 32, and his wife Ann on 18 July 1860 aged 83, being buried at Beddgelert.

Evans the Botanist and Richards the Guide

The Reverend John Evans (fl. 1768-1810s), originally of Lydney in Gloucestershire, made his botanical tour of North Wales in 1798 and on entering Wales from Shrewsbury he travelled by way of Newtown, Bala, Dolgellau, Barmouth, Harlech and northwards into the heart of Snowdonia. Harlech is described as 'a few miserable cottages on the top of a bare rock', where he records, probably among the sand dunes, the sharp rush (*Juncus acutus*) wild cabbage (*Brassica oleracea*) which used to grow on the cliffs below the castle but has not been recorded recently, and enchanter's nightshade (*Circaea lutetiana*), which was seen inside the castle and of which is added the following footnote. 'This plant called Enchanters Night Shade, was, in ages of ignorance, celebrated in the mysteries of witchcraft, and for raising the Devil.'

Since the Inn at Harlech offered no sleeping accommodation such as the botanist had been accustomed to, and sleeping on a bed of rushes laid on a bare floor did not appeal to him, a decision was made to proceed to Tan y Bwlch. While enquiring after a guide to lead him there he had the good fortune to meet a local man who could speak English fluently, a rare thing then in those parts, and after learning that the normal guide was absent the man agreed to lead them to Tan y Bwlch. John Richards proved himself a competent and reliable leader which left Evans with no regrets of having hired him, 'as some have done before us, that after employing a guide, they were obliged to give him information of the way'. Evans in his work provides an interesting account of Richards' career, and the reasons for his resorting to working as a guide.

John Richards was a native of Harlech, and had learned from his father a trade which combined that of skinner, breeches maker and glover. When hard times affected the industry the family was forced to seek other means of earning a living, and they turned to the wool trade, an idea which probably stemmed from the selling of wool remnants at the skinners yard. On receiving the bequest of a few hundred pounds on the death of his father in law, Richards' business flourished and the annual returns gradually increased, connections having been formed with London dealers. The dream of eventually being able to acquire a small estate was becoming more realisable as he was able to provide a better standard of living for the family who were by then being regarded as among the most prosperous in the area.

In an attempt to expand the business, Richards began to change his former London connections for others whom he thought would be more advantageous to him, and this for a time increased the demand for wool from the local farmers. Then the situation took a turn for the worse; delays in the receiving of payments forced Richards to try and obtain credit wherever he could, while at the same time the local farmers who supplied the wool were waiting to be paid. On demanding from the London businessmen an explanation for the decline in trade he was informed of the failure and closure of a business concern in Europe, and that when the affairs of that had been properly dealt with he would receive his entitled dividend as would the other creditors. He was now faced with the collapse of his business plus the constant demand for payment made by a number of poor farmers; he saw before him the gloomy prospect of life imprisonment should he be prosecuted. He called a meeting with the farmers and laid before them all his correspondence which explained the reasons for his business collapse. After much discussion it was realized that the problem had not arisen as a result of any dishonesty on the part of John Richards and the farmers unanimously decided that any debts would from that moment be written off. He was allowed to retain his furniture and stock of leather, so that he could continue with his glove making trade and in addition they promised to give what support they could to the family.

The once booming glove making trade had for some time been on the decline in North Wales as a result of English glove makers buying up all the leather and manufacturing a superior and cheaper glove by using more modern methods. 'Richards,' wrote Evans, 'was therefore reduced to the precarious emolument arising from the few journies he took in the summer months as a mountain guide, and the low profits upon a few strong country gloves, made during the winter, to support a sick wife and five children.'

Evans engaged Richards to guide him to Tan y Bwlch that evening and the path they took started steeply up the hillside behind Harlech, which by all accounts was 'a difficult stair-case path . . . which led over the trackless plain known to our guide by several upright stones called Maen Hirion'. (Meini Hirion). The route took them past Llandecwyn (where the moonlight reflected on the waters of the lake) and by following a track through a deep glen and crossing a stream near Felinrhyd they finally emerged on the turnpike road close to the village of Maentwrog. Here they crossed the bridge over the Dwyryd and arrived at the inn at Tan y Bwlch at 2 o'clock in the morning.

After spending the night at the inn at Tan y Bwlch, and the following day resting the horses, Evans, under the guidance of John Richards set out to complete the journey to Beddgelert, described by the botanist as 'eight miles of the worst road in the Principality', where they arrived soaked to the skin after experiencing a severe mountain storm. Evans, like Aikin, records observing the royal fern (*Osmunda regalis*) on the way, and he also notes the virtues of the bog-myrtle (*Myrica gale*). 'The poor inhabitants are not inattentive to its virtues; they term it Bwrli, or the emetic plant, and use it for this purpose. An infusion of the leaves as tea, and an external application of them to the abdomen, are considered as a certain and efficacious vermifuge. It is made a substitute for hops, in brewing: a decoction is used in the '*morbus pedicularis*', and in the vulgar species of herpes. It furnishes a yellow dye for woollen cloth; and by its powerful odour is fatal to moths and bugs.' Carolus Linnaeus is quoted as suggesting that camphor could be had from this plant, and the cones when boiled produce a waxy substance which, given that it was gathered in sufficient quantities, could be used to make candles. Withering (1796), quoting from Thomas Pennant's *Tours in Wales*, mentions how the Welsh people made use of it by laying the branches across their beds to keep away the fleas.

The difficulties surmounted, they finally arrived at Aberglaslyn and it was not long before they came to Beddgelert which was 'a few straggling houses' among which the inn was marked only by a sign reading 'The Guide to Snowdon lives here'. Their clothes were laid to dry before the fire while they ate their meal of fried eggs and bacon in bed, and refreshed also by what Evans describes as mugs of 'excellent cwrw', or Welsh beer. Apart from relating the story of Gelert and how it became connected with the village, followed by a brief history of the Church, Evans appears not to have spent much time at Beddgelert and is soon on the road to Caernarfon describing Nant Colwyn and the lake of the floating island (Llyn y Dywarchen) the tale of which is first recorded by Giraldus in 1188, and which Evans takes great delight in substantiating.

Bron y Fedw, the 'guide's house', at the start of one of the Snowdon paths is dismissed with just a brief reference, but on the road between Betws Garmon and Caernarfon the state of cottages of Snowdonia induces Evans to give a lengthy and detailed description of them. Compared to the cottages of Meirionnydd, the Caernarfonshire ones were in his opinion much worse, being built with turf or clay and chopped rushes except in the mountainous parts where stones, being more readily available, were used. The shape was described as being 'generally oblong' and consisting of one long room, the walls rising to about six feet above ground level with a roof made of heath or rushes laid upon rafters of 'maiden poles not even stripped of their bark'. Smoke from the peat fire usually filled the room before it found its way out through a hole in the roof, or through the doorway which in bad weather was blocked by a door made from 'a few watlings and rushes'. Evans goes on to describe the slightly better houses of the farmers, which had in addition a couple of bedrooms built in the loft, and a partition which divided the long room into two parts, but adds, 'even here, pigs, asses, and other domestic animals, take up their abode and form part of the family'. The botanist entered one of these hovels out of curiosity, and saw the family gathered around a small fire of peat about to start their supper of potatoes and 'diod griafol', . . . a drink made from the berries of the mountain ash (*Sorbus aucuparia*). Such scenes of abject poverty made a deep impression on Evans, and he makes known these feelings of disgust in his writings.

'Such are the dwellings in which part of the inhabitants of the most opulent and powerful nation upon earth at present live, and in which the Genius of

Virtue and Content seems to delight to dwell.' Despite these hardships the people that Evans met on his travels were generally cheerful and content, and he concludes his account of his meeting with the following quotation: 'Man wants but little, nor that little long'.

His description of the town of Caernarfon includes a list of the plants he saw while inspecting the various sites of historical interest. On a salt marsh opposite the castle, which has long since disappeared following the growth of the town, he found sea plantain (*Plantago maritima*) buck's-horn plantain (*Plantago coronopus*), sea arrowgrass (*Triglochin maritima*), brookweed (*Samolus valerandi*), sea-milkwort (*Glaux maritima*), Portland spurge (*Euphorbia portlandica*) and, on the shore near Llanfaglan, sea stork's-bill (*Erodium maritimum*) glasswort (*Salicornia agg.*) and sea campion (*Silene uniflora*).

Unlike most of the touring botanists of the same period, Evans did not climb Snowdon, nor did he succeed in reaching any of the sites which are noted for their variety of plants. Despite waiting a fortnight for the weather to improve, the opportunity did not present itself, and so he reluctantly gave up, confining his researches to the lower areas instead. Following the 'vale of the Seiont' as he calls it he records finding the fragrant orchid (*Gymnadenia conopsea*) and the small white orchid (*Pseudorchis albida*), a plant first recorded from these parts by John Ray in 1670.

Evans came on horseback to Cwm y Glo from Caernarfon, and took a boat from the lower end of Llyn Padarn to Pont y bala; the point where the two lakes meet close to Dolbadarn Castle. His botanical finds from this particular habitat include awlwort (*Subularia aquatica*), white water-lily, (*Nymphaea alba*) quillwort, (*Isoetes lacustris*) branched bur-reed (*Sparganium erectum*) and floating water-plantain (*Luronium natans*). The latter-named plant is the rarest and most interesting of the list, an earlier record of it appears in the 1789 edition of Camden's *Britannia*, 'in the great lake below the old castle at Llanberris'. This site must have been well known to the early botanists. John Wynne Griffith of Garn records it also: 'In a small rivulet on the west of the lower lake at Llanberris, about ½ a mile from the old castle.' Hugh Davies describes it not as a rarity but as a plant seldom seen in flower, especially so on the Isle of Anglesey. This he attributes 'to the extreme variableness of the depth of water in a level country, where lakes and rivers have no supply but immediately from the sky. In the month of May or June, this plant may be seen drawn by a stream to the length of many feet, from three to ten, or even more, where, at the end of six or eight weeks, the water being often so very much reduced as in some places not to cover the bed of the river, we can scarcely perceive any traces of it.' Davies records seeing the plant in Llyn Coron and one of the lakes near Valley, but it is now extinct in these localities according to Roberts (1982). It was recorded by the writer from Llyn Cwellyn near Betws

Garmon in 1989 but has not been seen at its old 'Dolbadarn' site near Llanberis since the building of the Hydro Power Electric Scheme there. John Evans' botanical rambles around the Nant Peris area is rewarded with such finds as Welsh poppy, *(Meconopsis cambrica)* ivy-leaved bellflower, *(Wahlenbergia hederacea)* scurvy grass, (recorded by Evans as *'Cochlearia Greenlandica')* lesser skullcap, *(Scutellaria minor)* The filmy-fern, *(Hymenophyllum wilsonii/H.tunbrigense)* parsley fern, *(Cryptogramma crispa)* oak fern, *(Gymnocarpium dryopteris)* field gentian, *(Gentianella campestris)* moss campion, *(Silene acaulis)* black spleenwort, *(Asplenium adiantum-nigrum)* wall rue, *(Asplenium ruta-muraria)* spring sandwort *(Minuartia verna)* holly fern *(Polystichum lonchitis)* northern bedstraw, *(Galium boreale)* and black alpine-sedge, *(Carex atrata)*. The scurvygrass recorded by Evans as *'Cochlearia Greenlandica'* was most probably a variety of the common scurvygrass *(Cochlearia officinalis)* which is found growing in a number of localities in Snowdonia. Withering (1796) doubts that the specimens collected from Wales by botanists and named *'Cochlearia groenlandica'* were in fact the true plant. He points out that the common scurvygrass taken from Wales and other mountainous parts of the British Isles and transplanted in his garden yearly produced flowers, compared with the true *'Cochlearia groenlandica'* which was biennial. John Wynne Griffith of Garn, whose opinion Withering sought on the matter had this to say: 'The Cochlearia groenlandica is certainly not an annual. I cultivated it 3 or 4 years, during which time it retained its diminutive state, which gave me reason to suppose it distinct from the C.officinalis; but I have since repeated the experiment, and it becomes as large as the C.officinalis.'

The scurvygrass *(Cochlearia)* group of plants can still cause problems to botanists and *C. groenlandica* is today included with *C.officinalis* forming a very variable aggregate species.

There is a cliff on the Carneddau range which is named 'Clogwyn Sgyrfi' (Scurvygrass cliff) and in former days, shepherds used to gather the plant leaves and eat them with their bread and butter as a sandwich.

Evans, though unable to climb Snowdon himself, gives a description of the various routes taken by the guides during this period. These routes were related to Evans by a friend. 'Ride to Cwm y Glo in the parish of Llanrug; take a boat up the lake of Llyn Padarn; land in the little Isthmus, between this and Llyn Peris, near Dolbadarn Castle; there take your guide and ascend by Ceunant Mawr, or the great chasm . . . Climb up along the South side of the ridge, that seperates Cwm Peris from Cwm Brwynog; thence ascend in sight of Llyn du yr Arddu, which you must leave on your right. The steep rock over this lake called Clogwyn du yr Arddu, i.e. the black rock above the Arddu, is celebrated for a great variety of rare plants. Ascending a steep and difficult pass, called Llechwedd y Re, you arrive at a cold spring, called Llyn coch, which is within a mile of the highest summit called y Wydd fa . . . the steep and almost inaccessible crags on the North side of this peak, are termed Clogwyn y Garnedd; and known to Lloyd and Ray for the habitats of alpine plants.'

The second route to the summit which is given by Evans is that of the Snowdon Ranger path, and although not known by its modern name at that time, he describes it as the usual ascent.

The 'Bedd Kelert' route is 'extremely steep and dangerous' and the terrors of crossing Clawdd Coch and Bwlch Main are vividly described. The plants listed by Evans as growing on Clogwyn y Garnedd and Clogwyn Du'r Arddu are also included on the authority of the same anonymous friend who gave him details of the Snowdon paths. Of the nineteen plants named as growing on Clogwyn y Garnedd only ten have been substantiated by subsequent plant hunters. These are the Snowdon lily, (*Lloydia serotina*) alpine saw-wort, (*Saussurea alpina*) alpine mouse-ear, (*Cerastium alpinum*) arctic mouse-ear, (*Cerastium arcticum*) starry saxifrage, (*Saxifraga stellaris*) alpine saxifrage, (*Saxifraga nivalis*) oblong woodsia (*Woodsia ilvensis*) alpine woodsia, (*Woodsia alpina*) Welsh poppy, (*Meconopsis cambrica*) and dwarf juniper (*Juniperis communis ssp.alpina*); the latter named known to grow close to, if not on this cliff. The remainder include: alpine catchfly, (*Lychnis alpina*) which in Britain is a very rare plant found only in Cumberland and Angus; forked spleenwort, (*Asplenium septentrionale*) a small fern found in various parts of Snowdonia but not on this particular cliff; royal fern, (*Osmunda regalis*) recorded from the area but not from Clogwyn y Garnedd; mountain pansy, (*Viola lutea*) mountain avens, (*Dryas octopetala*) yellow saxifrage (*Saxifraga aizoides*); of which the 'Dryas' is the only plant confirmed as being extant in Snowdonia.

For Clogwyn Du'r Arddu he names but two plants, the stone bramble (*Rubus saxatilis*) and northern rock-cress (*Arabis petraea*), the latter named being first noted on this cliff by Thomas Johnson during his botanical excursion of 1639.

Two other well known botanical hunting grounds mentioned by Evans are Llyn y Cŵn and Trigyfylchau Rocks. The exact locality of the latter is by now obscure, but were frequently refered to by both Lhuyd and Brewer. The Llyn y Cŵn area still produces such plants as water lobelia (*Lobelia dortmanna*) and the three-flowered rush (*Juncus triglumis*); the cliffs around Cwm Idwal, where Trigyfylchau was located, are the stronghold of the rare Snowdon lily (*Lloydia serotina*) which appears on Evans' plant list for this area. Also included are plants which seem to have been either overlooked by other botanists or inserted erroneously; namely the hoary whitlowgrass, (*Draba incana*) alpine mouse-ear (*Cerastium alpinum*) and spring bulbocodium (*Bulbocodium vernum*), as there have been no subsequent records of them from this locality. It is therefore evident that the Reverend John Evans relied on other sources for much of the plant information which he published in his book *Tour through North Wales* in 1800, with a second edition appearing in 1802. He was by all accounts a competent and highly regarded botanist, graduating B.A. at Oxford in 1792 and later becoming Master of the Academy, Kingsdown; he supplied Turner and Dillwyn with plant references for their *Botanist's Guide* published in 1805. His anonymous friend from whom he received the names of some of the Alpine plants of Snowdonia proved an unreliable source, and it is regrettable that he did not venture out on to the high places and carry out his own observations.

Bingley's Botanical Tours

The Reverend William Bingley (1774-1823) who visited North Wales in 1798 and 1801 appended a catalogue of plants to his *Tour round North Wales . . .* ' published in 1800, and also in the later edition of 1804 entitled *North Wales: its scenery, antiquities, customs, etc.* The *'Flora Cambrica'* as he calls it, was 'a Systematic Catalogue of the more uncommon Welsh plants . . . ' which included their known habitats and their flowering times.

William Bingley was born at Doncaster, Yorkshire in January 1774 and graduated B.A. at Cambridge in 1799. He became a 'Fellow of the Linnaean Society' in 1800 and was Curate at Christchurch Priory, Hampshire from 1802 until 1816 after which he moved to London and was Minister at Fitzroy Chapel, Charlotte Street until his death in 1823. His first visit to North Wales was undertaken during the summer recess of 1798 while he was a student at Cambridge, and travelling by coach to Chester he began his tour by following 'the great Irish road' through St Asaph, Conwy and Bangor to Caernarfon, where he stayed for a time and made his excursions to the mountains and visited parts of Anglesey. He then planned and followed a route which took him to Harlech, Barmouth, Dolgellau, Machynlleth, Llanidloes, Newtown, Montgomery, Welshpool, Oswestry, Wrexham and Mold where he turned inland to Rhuthun, Llangollen, Corwen and Bala returning to Cambridge via Shrewsbury in the month of September.

This first visit made a deep impression on the young botanist and he returned in 1801, to stop four months during which time he walked around the counties of Caernarfon, Meirionnydd, and Anglesey between the months of June and September. 'Previously to my first journey' he wrote, 'I had made several tours through nearly all the romantic parts of the North of England. I can, however, with truth declare, that, taken in the whole, I have not found these by any means so interesting as four of the six counties of North Wales, namely, Denbighshire, Caernarvonshire, Meirionethshire and Anglesea'.

Bingley made his excursion chiefly as a pedestrian but at times he found it more convenient to use horses or carriages. He is, however, quick to point out the advantages of walking, especially when the places of attraction are inaccessible to carriages and horses. Bingley's companion and guide during most of his rambles in Snowdonia was the Reverend Peter Bailey Williams, (1763-1836) rector of the parishes of Llanrug and Llanberis, whose various interests, like the visitor included local history and botany. Williams knew the country well, and was able to introduce Bingley to the more interesting characters who dwelt in the two parishes, and the latter being a prolific writer meticulously noted down all these observations to include in his forthcoming book. Bingley, like the Reverend John Evans who has been mentioned previously, was invited to visit the farms of the area, the first of which lay in

Cwm y Glo, and it proved to be no different to the home which Evans commented on during his journey from Betws Garmon to Caernarfon. 'I enterd at a small gate, and first observed a wretched hovel for his cattle: the hay rick was formed by a large slate, placed near one side, with its edge on the ground: the roof was broken in and damaged, so that only one corner afforded shelter to the miserable beasts from the fury of the mountain storms . . . A path between two rude stone walls, adorned with holly hedges, led me to the dwelling. The door was so low, that I was obliged to stoop considerably to enter; and coming out of a bright sun-shine, it was not till some time had elapsed that I was able to distinguish any thing in this hut, except the gleam of light that came down the chimney. This was at least equal to what the six small panes of glass in the window afforded. On the open hearth were a few peat-ashes, the remains of a fire with which the old man had a little while before cooked his dinner. The frame of the roof was formed by branches of trees fixed to larger timbers by straw or hay-bands. This frame was covered with sods, and the whole with slates, which, in the mountains, are obtained in great plenty. The furniture consisted of an old bed, an oak chest, a range of shelves for such poor eating utensils as were necessary in this lowly habitation, some old earthen vessels, some dingy pewter dishes, and a few other things . . . ' Bingley on reflection chose a few lines of Goldsmith's: 'Man wants but little here below, etc.,' which were the very lines quoted by Evans who saw a similar Snowdonian habitat in the same year as Bingley. On the same day Williams led Bingley to the cottage of a lame old woman who lived close to the farm they had just visited and the traveller's only reason for mentioning Mary Morgan is the fact that she used the chimney of her house as a means of entry whenever she mislaid the key of the door.

Bingley, accompanied by Williams, took a boat from Cwm y Glo to Llanberis, where the local man related the story of Margaret Evans who lived in Penllyn near the lower end of Llyn Padarn. Marged uch Ifan or Peggy Evans, as she was also called, hailed from the Nantlle Valley where she kept an Inn called Telyrnia which was situated close to the lake below the farm of Gelli Ffrydiau, Nantlle, at the time when the copper mines of Drws y Coed flourished. She later moved to the Llanberis area, where she held a contract to convey the copper ore down the lakes. Margaret was also a blacksmith, shoe maker, boat builder and maker of harps, and the finest hunter in all Snowdonia keeping a pack of hounds for tracking down foxes, and for every fox she killed she carved a notch on her wooden mantlepiece. She was immortalised by Pennant as the 'Queen of the Lakes' and at the age of seventy-two was the best wrestler in the country while also being fond of playing the harp and violin. It must be noted that none of the 'tours' writers, Pennant included, actually met Margaret, and the tales of her exploits were related to the travellers by the guides and other local people. The 'Queen of the Lakes', however will always remain part of the Snowdonian folklore. An entry in the Llanddeiniolen Parish Register dated 24 January 1793 records the burial of Margaret Evans, aged 91, of Penllyn. (G.A.S. XPE 293)

There were two houses at Llanberis during this time which provided travellers with refreshments. One belonged to John Closs, a Yorkshireman who had as a young man travelled into North Wales with some cattle and decided to stay. John Closs was a 'grey headed old man' at the time of Bingley's visit and the inn was kept by his son Robert, who, when occasion demanded, took up the role of a mountain guide to supplement the family income. Morris Pritchard, the parish clerk, kept the other house and he also was a competent part-time guide.

The inns did not provide any beds for the travellers and the only food available was bread, butter and cheese and bacon and eggs. Bingley called at John Closs's house during his first visit to Llanberis and relates his novel experiences at the dinner table. John Closs, his wife and son and daughter sat at one table eating their bread and milk while the botanist sat at another table enjoying his bread and butter and satisfying an appetite brought on after a day among the hills. His meal was soon interrupted by the intrusion of a 'large overgrown old sow' which entered the room and began to devour, rather noisily, her own dinner from a bucket which the daughter had placed before her. After this experience, Bingley vowed that in future he would bring his own food and enjoy it in the solitude of the countryside.

Bingley does not mention whether or not he stayed at the house of Morris Pritchard, but he does speak very highly of his prowess as a guide. 'I found him well acquainted with the mountains, and a much more intelligent man than guides in general are. He does not speak English well, but his civility and attention are a sufficient compensation for this defect.' Morris Pritchard was known to other visiting botanists and was often employed by them to gather alpine plants from the surrounding mountains, a task which was frequently undertaken by the guides. Despite Bingley's claim that the parish clerk did not speak good English the Reverend Peter Bailey Williams nevertheless wrote to him in English; this letter is dated 'Whitmonday 1794', and reads, 'I understand the Parishoners turn cattle into the Churchyard and seem to look upon it as their property, but I shall soon let them know that it is my Freehold, and in the meantime I require and charge you to keep the Churchyard locked and not suffer any one to turn sheep, calves or any kind of cattle into it. Did Mr Morgan keep either cow or horse, I should have suffered him to have the use of it. When Owen David comes up to take tythe lambs I shall give him leave to turn them in for a day or two. I am, Yours, etc., Peter Williams. P.S Either you or Mr Morgan must keep the key of the Churchyard.' Morris Pritchard died 9 February 1818, leaving a sickly daughter and arrears of rent amounting to £9. Harry David, the old guide's grandson, later applied to be given the tenancy of

Gallt y Llan and reside there with the daughter on the understanding that the arrears of rent be settled. In the above letter the Rev. Williams mentions John Morgan the curate, whom Bingley visited during one of his excursions to Llanberis. The Reverend John Morgan came to Llanberis in 1772 and served twenty-nine years as Curate. He died at the age of 58 and was buried in the Churchyard on 30 March 1801. Bingley found the curate 'engaged over an old folio volume of sermons' in his small cottage situated a short distance from the Church. The cottage was divided into two parts, a kitchen and a bedroom, the latter also being used as a study where the curate worked and housed his small library. He was dressed, according to the botanist in a 'blue coat that long had been worn threadbare, and in various places exhibited marks of the industry of his wife, a pair of antique corderoy breeches, and a black waistcoat, and round his head was tied a blue handkerchief.' He supported his family on a salary of £40 per annum, plus the produce gained from his small farm and was a very contented man, popular and greatly respected by the parishioners. He was a very popular preacher and his reputation spread to other parts of Snowdonia iducing people to travel great distances to hear his sermons.

Bingley's botanical excursion to Clogwyn Du'r Arddu developed into what today would be termed a rock climb. The Reverend Peter Bailey Williams, who led Bingley on most of these mountain walks, suggested that they climbed the precipice to look for more plants. All went well at the beginning, but the visitor soon became aware of the dangers involved when he tried to pull himself up and the rock on which he had put his weight gave way. He only just managed to save himself by grabbing at a 'tuft of rushes'. They had climbed about 300 feet up the cliff when they realized that it was too dangerous to try and retrace their steps, so they decided to try to overcome the difficult pitch which lay directly above them. Williams, who led, had on a pair of strong boots with nailed soles, and with some difficulty managed to overcome the crux to gain a secure position higher up. The local man carried a small basket which was used to carry provisions and the plant specimens they had collected on the way up, and this was held securely to his body by means of a leather belt around the waist. Williams took off the belt and used it to haul Bingley over the difficult part of the cliff after which they were able to continue to the top of the precipice without further incident. From there they followed the Snowdon Ranger path to the summit of Snowdon.

Bingley goes on to list the plants found growing on Clogwyn y Garnedd, the steep cliff which faces north-east directly below the summit of 'yr Wyddfa'; a site which was known to both Ray and Lhuyd for its uncommon alpine plants. He lists 25 species as growing on this cliff, and it is a much more accurate and credible account than the one Evans published in his 'tour' of 1798. Evans included his plant list on the testimony of his anonymous friend and never ventured to Clogwyn y Garnedd himself. Bingley does not state catagorically that he visited the cliff, but stresses the hazards which had to be encountered in doing so. 'There is at all times some difficulty in searching them, [the cliffs of Clogwyn y Garnedd] but when the rocks are rendered slippery from heavy mists or rain, this becomes, from the insecurity of the footing, greatly increased. A list of plants that have been found here may not be unacceptable, at least to a young botanist.' It can therefore be assumed from the wording of the above sentence that the plant list had been given to Bingley by Williams or some other botanist.

Bingley then ascended Snowdon by way of Cwmglas Mawr, a wild hollow high above the Pass of Llanberis which has the finest variety of plants in the whole district, but the only ones mentioned in this chapter are awlwort (*Subularia aquatica*), quillwort (*Isoetes lacustris*) and water lobelia (*Lobelia dortmanna*), which were observed in Llyn Bach on the way up. This lake used to be called Llyn Ffynnon Frech up until the present century, and the hollow we know today as Cwmglas Mawr would not in Bingley's day have been known by this name. In those days Cwm Glas was the name given to the lower part of the Llanberis Pass from the area around the farm of Cwmglas Bach up to and including the regions below Bwlch Coch, and Bingley's plant records for Cwmglas Mawr, which appear in his *Flora Cambrica*, would be given as being found on 'rocks above Ffynnon Frech', or, 'on Crib y Ddescil, near Llanberis' and the quillwort was described as growing in 'Ffynnon Frech, a small pool in the mountains betwixt Llanberis and Snowdon', not as we would say today; 'in Cwmglas Mawr'. Bwlch Coch is situated between the pinnacles of Crib Goch and the long ridge which culminates on Crib y Ddisgl, the second highest peak in Snowdonia. The route followed by Bingley took him from Bwlch Coch across the southern slopes of Crib y Ddisgl to Bwlch Glas, above the lake of Llyn Glaslyn, which he mis-names Llyn y Cwm Glas; this lake was known in those days as Ffynnon Las as well as Glaslyn. He then followed the Pony track from Bwlch Glas to the summit, and returned to Llanberis by descending the steep slope directly above the village of Nant Peris (called Llanberis in Bingley's day), a route so rugged and unpleasant that it made him wish that he had followed the pony track to Dolbadarn Castle, instead of using the short cut.

The following day saw this intrepid botanist ascending Snowdon once again, but this time from the opposite side of the mountain. Bingley rode from Llanberis to Betws Garmon and began the day's excursion from Bron y Fedw, the guide's house near Llyn Cwellyn. The horses were left in the care of servants near Llyn Ffynnon y Gwas, at the foot of the main climb-as was the custom with visitors who used this path-and the party continued on foot up the rocky shoulder towards the summit. Bingley found this path very tiring, either as the result of the previous day's exertions, or from the ruggedness of the terrain. During the years which followed the Snowdon Ranger Path, as it was later to be called, was improved in order to transport the copper ore from the mines near Llyn Glaslyn to Caernarfon. The ore was carried by the miners in bags to Bwlch Glas where it was transferred onto small sledges which were then dragged by horses down to the road at Betws Garmon, there to be carted to Caernarfon. The new sledge-way made the ascent of Snowdon from Llyn Cwellyn much easier for the tourist, but the transporting of copper ore was later transferred to a more convenient route on the northern side of the mountain when the new road connecting Llanberis and Pen y gwryd was opened, to which the Miners track was built joining it at Gorffwysfa (Pen y Pass).

Bingley enjoyed fine weather during the morning and the clear views from the summit more than compensated for the hard toil up the rocky path. The guide, whom Bingley does not name was, most probably Ellis Griffith of Bron y Fedw. He quite suddenly gave warning of an approaching storm and advised the party to prepare to descend the mountain immediately. Bingley admits to ridiculing the guide's warning at first, but later had enough reason to regret having done so. During the descent the party was overtaken by a severe mountain storm and the botanist was glad to have a moment to reflect upon the day's events as he rested in the guide's 'cottage' while waiting for his clothes to dry.

His aim to climb Snowdon by all the principal routes was fulfilled when he set out from Ffridd Uchaf, a farm on the lower west facing side of the massif, along the old Beddgelert track. The path winds its way towards Llechog before reaching the summit by traversing Clawdd Coch and crossing Bwlch Main. This route is known today as the Rhyd Ddu path. The horses were left at the farm, and the visitors then walked as far as the site where later was built the 'Half-way House', a corrugated iron structure where refreshments could be acquired. The 18th century travellers however had to make do with a drink of water from a natural spring among the rocks, the last but one spring between there and the summit. This site is unique as being the only level patch of ground on a rugged mountainside, and legend has it that it was the site of an ancient temple called 'Mur Murianau'. Scattered over this site are the remains of several circular stone huts (Cytiau Gwyddelod) built up at a much later date to be used as sheepfolds. To the south west a line of rocks form a wall which if followed will be seen to enclose the whole site, and on a rocky elevation at one end a large clog-shaped rock is seen resting on three smaller stones, one at each corner; the whole structure having the appearance of an altar. Bingley's guide during this excursion was William Lloyd of Beddgelert who was also the village schoolmaster, and when the Beddgelert Hotel, later to be called the Royal Goat, was built he served there as a waiter. He advertised his summer vocation with the aid of a poster displayed on the door of the Inn which read 'William Lloyd, conductor to Snowdon, Moel Hebog, Dinas Emrys, Llanberis pass, the lakes, waterfalls, &c &c. Collector of crystals and fossils, and all natural curiosities in these regions. Dealer in superfine woollen hose, socks, gloves &c'. William Lloyd died in 1804 leaving his wife with a considerable quantity of fossils to sell.

There are no rare alpine plants mentioned by Bingley during this ascent, the whole account being dominated by a description of the views and the terrain over which the route passes. Like Evans (whose description of the path, it must be remembered, is given on the authority of another) Bingley's account of passing over the Clawdd Coch-Bwlch Main section is greatly dramatised. 'This narrow pass, not more than ten or twelve feet across, and two or three hundred yards in length, was so steep, that the eye reached on each side, down the whole extent of the mountain . . . in some parts of it, if a person held a large stone in each hand, and let them both fall at once, each might roll a quarter of a mile, and thus, when they stopped, they might be more than half a mile asunder'. Bingley, however, is quick to point out that he was not at all afraid of crossing this ridge, at least during the day time, but that a night ascent along the same route was a different matter. The chapter also included stories, probably narrated to him by the guide, of the terror and fright experienced by other visitors whilst negotiating the ridge; people having passed over it during the hours of darkness, unaware of the exposure on either side, refusing to return by the same way when they were coming down in the morning. There were also tales of the gentleman who, being so alarmed, resorted to crawl across on hands and knees.

William Lloyd, having guided the party to the summit, led the party back to Beddgelert by returning over Clawdd Coch and continuing directly down the South Ridge to Bwlch Cwm Llan, and from there to Nantgwynant. Bingley's only mention of plants on this trip concerns a group of children collecting the berries from the mountain ash (*Sorbus aucuparia*) in Cwm Llan. The guide William Lloyd then explained to him that the berries were crushed and left in water for two weeks at the end of which time it was ready to consume. This drink, called 'diod griafol', after the Welsh name for mountain ash 'pren criafol', was mentioned in the previous chapter when discussing the Reverend John Evans and his tour of North Wales in 1798.

Guided by Peter Bailey Williams, Bingley completed a traverse of part of the Glyder range climbing Tryfan, Glyder Fach and Glyder Fawr which he declares to be 'by far the most laborious walk that I ever ventured upon in the course of one day'. Their excursion began at Nant Peris at 7 in the morning and on reaching Llyn y Cŵn they met a group of men digging up peat, one of whom was the son of one of the Llanberis guides. The peat was conveyed by horses to the verge of the steep descent, where it was transferred onto sledges. The men would then push the sledges down to the valley floor, running to gain speed where practicable and braking by moving the sledge from side to side whenever a steeper gradient caused too great a velocity.

From Llyn y Cŵn, the party walked down into Cwm Idwal, passing below the Devil's Kitchen on the way. Bingley refers to the chasm by its Welsh name 'Twll Du', explaining that the small holes in the rocks at its base are known as the 'Devil's Pots'; being the reason for the place to be sometimes known as the Devil's Kitchen.

The ascent of Tryfan was undertaken from Cwm Bochlwyd; the steep rocky appearance at first creating doubts in the minds of the two clergymen if such an attempt would be practicable. However, after a scramble of about three quarters of an hour, which called for frequent use of hand-holds, the pair eventually stood next to 'Adam and Eve', the two conspicuous columnar boulders which crown the summit. Williams climbed to the top of one of the rocks, and, as Bingley watched apprehensively, calmly stepped from one to the other. This feat was apparently frequently performed by a 'female of an adjacent parish'. The summit of Glyder Fach, the next mountain visited, compelled the agile Williams to explore the heaped pile of variously shaped boulders that compose the summit, and one in particular, known today as the 'Cantelever', a long flat projecting rock, moved as he jumped on it.

They crossed the 'Waen oer' to the summit of Glyder Fawr and continued their way back to the vale of Llanberis at 8 o'clock in the evening, after spending fourteen hours among the hills.

At the end of this chapter Bingley listed 52 plants that he saw about Llyn y Cŵn and the Devil's Kitchen area; and unlike the Reverend John Evans', there were no plants included which was not already known to occur in Snowdonia. It is evident from his writings that Bingley derived great pleasure from walking the mountains of Snowdonia and is critical of many of his contemporaries for overstating the difficulties likely to be met with during such rambles. He dismisses the carrying of strong sticks with a spike at the end as being unnecessary, and like wise the wearing of nailed boots. He advises the tourist to make an early start, 'to be upon the journey by five or six o'clock in the morning', the advantage of this being that there would be sufficient time to stop and rest frequently to admire the changing scenery as height was gained. To undertake any journey into the mountains without a guide, would in his opinion, be foolhardy: 'a sudden change in the weather might render the attempt extremely perilous to a stranger'. The guides, being familiar with the mountains, knew the course of the paths by the shape of certain rocks, and the flow of the streams. These 'waymarks' had been memorized over the years, and were useful when low cloud and mist covered the way.

Bingley's *Flora Cambrica* consists of 58 pages where 472 plants plus several varieties were named. All the 'classical' habitats of Snowdonia are mentioned when an uncommon plant is dealt with, these being:

Habitat	Number of plants listed
Clogwyn y Garnedd	16
Clogwyn Du'r Arddu	7
Cwm Idwal — Twll Du (Devil's Kitchen)	23
Llyn y Cŵn	10

To these are added Glyder Fawr, Snowdon, Crib y Ddisgl, Cwmbrwynog, the two lakes in Cwmglas, Ffynnon Frech and Ffynnon Felen, and the long forgotten sites of Creigiau Hysfa Bengam and Trigyfylchau, which are thought to be situated on Glyder Fawr, to the south-east of the Devil's Kitchen chasm.

A great number of the plants recorded by Evans and Bingley appear in various editions of Nicholson's *Cambrian Traveller's Guide*. By the end of the 18th century most of the interesting flowering plants of Snowdonia had been discovered, as too were the richest localities, the cliffs and 'cymoedd' of Snowdon and Glyder. These sites had been visited by generations of botanists from the days of Johnson, and each one had amassed records which others had built upon. Some outlying districts, however, remained botanically unexplored.

The Reverend Peter Bailey Williams

The Reverend Peter Bailey Williams (1763-1836), a native of Llandyfaelog, Carmarthen, (and son of Peter Williams the biblical commentator) became Rector of Llanrug and Llanberis in 1792 and remained there for the rest of his life, being buried in Llanrug Churchyard. He entered Jesus College, Oxford to read law, but decided during his first term to change his mind and become a Church minister. He was ordained Deacon by the Bishop of Gloucester in February 1788 and licenced to the curacy of Eastleach Martin. In November of the same year he was ordained Minister; the following month received a permanent curacy at Swinbrook, Oxfordshire. Early in 1790 he moved to Burford where he remained until his preferment to Llanrug and Llanberis, serving also in Betws Garmon from 1815 onwards. In September 1804 he married Hannah, the daughter of Henry and Ann Jones of Llanrwst and had one son, who, following his graduation became a curate for his father.

Peter Bailey Williams was a staunch conservative, and had no sympathies with the current revolutionary upheaval in France, and was, as would be expected, in favour of retaining the 'tithe' laws. He was Justice of Peace for the

Rev. Peter Bailey Williams (1763-1836)

county of Caernarfon, at a time when this office held a much wider range of responsibilities than it does today, yet despite his strong political beliefs he always stood firmly in support of the rights of the poor. He is remembered mainly for his literary and antiquarian interests and was a close friend of local poets like David Thomas of Waunfawr, (Dafydd Ddu Eryri 1759-1822) William Edwards (Gwilym Padarn 1786-1857) and his son Griffith Edwards (Gutyn Padarn 1812-1893) of Llanberis, Robert Parry (Robyn Ddu Eryri 1804-1892) of Caernarfon and Owen Williams (Owain Gwyrfai 1790-1874) of Waunfawr, as well as many others. His own poetical compositions leave a lot to be desired, and none of his attempts at translating Welsh poetry into English were successful.

He copied extensively from old manuscripts in the libraries of the county's most prominent families and avidly collected all kinds of old stories, legends and traditions. Most of his manuscripts later came to be in the possession of John Davies (Gwyneddon, 1832-1904) the printer and journalist and these are now kept at the University College Library at Bangor, entitled the 'Gwyneddon Manuscripts'. The remainder became part of John Humphreys Davies' large collection. Davies (1871-1926), a bibliographer, man of letters and educationist, was a foremost recognized authority on Welsh books and manuscripts, and his documents are today kept at the National Library of Wales, Aberystwyth under the title 'Cwrt Mawr Manuscripts'.

Of the travellers who visited North Wales during this period, two are known to have stayed in Williams' home at Pantafon, Llanrug: the Reverend William Bingley whom we have dealt with in the previous chapter, and Richard Fenton (1747-1821) the poet and topographical writer from Pembroke. Fenton made use of Williams' library at Pantafon, 'to satiate myself with his very curious and miscellaneous collections of Welsh History added much to my stock'. Another topographical writer who received help from Williams was William Catherall who in 1828 published his *History of North Wales*. In a letter to Walter Davies (Gwallter Mechain, 1761-1849; cleric, poet, antiquary and literary critic), Williams tells of how he wrote to Catherall, 'to point out some mistakes in his history of North Wales,' to which the writer replied that he had received no help from the people from whom he had requested assistance earlier. 'I began to assist him when he was about commencing the History of Anglesey and I have now gone through all the North Wales counties except Montgomeryshire', wrote Williams, who admitted to being in need of Davies' advice before completing his notes and submitting them to Catherall.

Nicholas Carlisle, author of the *Topographical Dictionary to the Dominion of Wales* was also indebted to Williams during his preparatory researches for his book.

There can be no doubt that Bailey Williams had a special interest in local history, and in 1821 he published the result of his researches in his book entitled *Tourist Guide through the County of Caernarvon containing a short sketch of its History, Antiquities, &c.*

The volume is in many ways similar to others already published about the topography of Wales, except that it deals with only one county. It has been said of the book that it lacks the detail needed to be a reliable guide-book for visitors, and is too disorderly an arrangement to qualify as a history book of high standard, as the sub-title claims. He also wrote an essay on the History of Anglesey, and another on the Monasteries and Abbeys of Wales.

Despite his own local knowledge Williams relied heavily on the work of Pennant for his guide book on Caernarfonshire. He was also indebted to Leland's *Itinerary*, first published by Thomas Hearne, 1710-12 and with later editions appearing in 1744, 1770 and 1906, and Nicholas Owen's *Caernarvonshire. A Sketch of its History, Antiquities, Mountains and Productions.* (1792). In comparing pages 14 to 17 of the *Tourist Guide* with *Pennant's Tours* (1883 ed. vol.iii pp 116-123) the text of the works would be found to be nearly identical. The chapter in question dealt with Conwy, but Williams relies on Pennant even when describing his home parishes of Llanrug and Llanberis. This practice is also much in evidence with most other topographical authors of the time, but why Williams, who had collected so much himself, chose to copy from other writers rather than use his own material is indeed a mystery.

His other interest was botany, and although he makes several references about the plants of Snowdonia and their habitats in his book, he decided to ask another local botanist, John Roberts of Caernarfon, and later Bangor, to prepare a list of plants to be included in the appendix of his *Tourist's Guide*.

Among the 'Gwyneddon Manuscripts' kept at the University of Wales, Bangor Library, is a list of plants compiled by the Reverend Peter Bailey Williams entitled 'Botany of Snowdon Plants'. This consists of the scientific and English plant names with a space left for the Welsh names to be added, and also a section for the localities of some of the less common. There are no plants listed which had not been recorded previously for the county nor are there any new localities.

In Bailey Williams' personal copy of Hugh Davies' *Welsh Botanology*, now in a private collection, there is a list of rare plants copied onto the margins of page xv which has been annotated by the original owner, and on other pages there are more plant names which appear under the heading: 'Indigenous plants in the vicinity of Carnarvon'. Also included are three herbal remedies, one for the cure of ague and the others for migraine and toothache; these were apparently copied from the old manuscript book of Hafod Uchtryd, Cardiganshire. The ague treatment consists of a drink made from dandelion (*Taraxacum*) leaves mixed with those of the common fumitory (*Fumaria officinalis*) which must be drunk 'hard during the morning and at noon'. For the migraine it is advised that the roots of the primrose (*Primula vulgaris*) and the leaves of betony

(*Stachys officinalis*) be used to block the nostrils 'each day of the week'. Toothache is said to be cured by boiling holly (*Ilex aquifolium*) leaves in springwater and inhaling the steam which arose from the pot.

In a letter dated 27 June 1828 Bailey Williams requests the help of William Wilson of Warrington, (1799-1871) another noted botanist, in sending him a list of plants which would be likely to be found on the mountains in readiness for a group of visiting botanists. Bailey Williams thus made arrangements for the visit. 'My intention is to employ a man to collect them at the lake, . . . at the beginning of next week. Mr N. [Newcome] has made a mistake as I am no Botanist . . . If you would have the kindness to give me a list of plants and their habitats. If you care to remain any time longer at Llanberis you would probably allow the Bearer Ellis Jones who speaks a little English & attend you up the mountains in order to collect some of the plants best adapted for this purpose.'

In addition to the 'Gwyneddon Mss' held at Bangor more of the Reverend Peter Bailey Williams' papers are among the manuscripts at the National Library of Wales, Aberystwyth. Among these writings is the tragic story of the death of young John Closs of Llanberis who perished on Moel Eilio on 17 December 1805. John was the seven year old son of Robert Closs, guide and landlord of the village inn at Llanberis (Nant Peris) who went to reside with his grandmother at Betws Garmon; the mother walking over occasionally to visit them. During one of these visits the young lad decided to follow his mother home to Nant Peris over the mountain, but without making his intention known to her or his grandmother. Snow began to fall, fine blinding snowflakes which soon covered the path and obscured the footprints of his mother. John Closs lost his way and began to wander. His body was eventually found following a search of two or three days near the summit of Moel Eilio, where he had perished presumably from hypothermia. He was buried at Nant Peris Churchyard and the poet David Thomas (Dafydd Ddu Eryri) composed the following 'englyn' which was carved on his tombstone:

Oerfel anochel fu'n achos — i Angau
Llym ingol, ymddangos —
Mantell niwl mewn tywyll nos
A dychryniad dechreunos.

Also preserved in the same manuscript is a list of the various cliffs, hills and ridges that Bailey Williams had diligently recorded from the inhabitants of the Nant Peris district.

'Rocks or Eminences on the S. & S.W. of Llanberis Village taking the whole length of the ridge or Buttress & commencing near Cwm Glas Ucha.
Y Gyrn Las

Llechwedd y Re
Brynn Pen y Llyn
Llechog
Clogwyn yr Ysgwydd
Y Bol Du
Y Tryfan Bach
Tryfan Mawr
Pen Carreg y Frân
Y Dderlwyn

Eminences N. of Do.
Y Glyder Fawr
Ysdol Felen
Braich Glas under it
Cwm y Nadroedd under that
Pen y Cerneu — North end of Glyder
Cwm Padrig
Llosgwrn — North of Pen y Foel
Pistill Gwynn between Pen y Foel & Glyder
Bryn Bras between Pen y Foel & Llosgwrn
Esgair y Ceunant
Garn o'r Pen y Garn.'

A few of the names appear on current O.S. maps, while the remainder has been lost or forgotten over the years.

'Cors y Bwrli' was a boggy tract of land near Dolbadarn Castle where the bog-myrtle (*Myrica gale*) grew in 'great plenty'. The bog takes its name from one of the Welsh names of this plant, 'bwrli'. The above is entered by Bailey Williams on a sheet under the heading 'Plants-Habitats'. He goes on to include the dwarf juniper (*Juniperis communis ssp alpina*) from 'the side of Glydair Fawr mountain & Crib Goch'; floating water-plantain (*Luronium natans*) 'in the great Lake below the Castle'; thrift (*Armeria maritima*) which he calls 'Mountain Thrift' on Clogwyn y Garnedd and 'on Clogwyn Du yn yr arddu'; roseroot (*Sedum rosea*) 'on a rock on the North side of Bwlch Glâs near the ascent to the Peak or Summit of Snowdon'; alpine saxifrage (*Saxifraga nivalis*) and starry saxifrage (*Saxifraga stellaris*) 'on Clogwyn y Garnedd i.e. north side of Snowdon'; the water-lilies (*Nymphaea alba* and *Nuphar lutea*) 'near Cwm y Glo in the lower Lake & River'. He concludes the page by saying 'There are great varieties of plants on the side of Allt Wenn above Mr Smith's Cottage.' The site probably referred to is the slopes of Fachwen, above Llyn Padarn.

Peter Bailey Williams served the parishioners of Llanrug and Llanberis for forty-four years. Among his varied interests were poetry, collecting and copying old manuscripts, local history, botany and agriculture. He was also an author and translator, and a prolific writer contributing numerous articles for Welsh and English journals on subjects which included religion, poetry and agricultural improvement. Mountaineers will remember Williams as the first man to lead a rock climb in Snowdonia. He and Bingley climbed the eastern terrace of Clogwyn Du'r Arddu in 1798, describing the use of hands and knees, the sudden grip of fear experienced when a hold loosened, and the use of a belt in the absence of a rope.

John Roberts Penclip, 'A Bygone Welsh Botanist'

The list of plants appended to *The Tourist's Guide through the County of Caernarvon* (1821) was the work of 'Mr John Roberts, Surgeon, Caernarvon' whose name appeared occasionally in botanical books and journals during the early part of the 19th century.

An enquiry, submitted by botanist A.A. Dallman (1883-1963) appeared in the *North Western Naturalist* (1926-March 31) under the heading 'A Bygone Welsh Botanist'. The note states that 'Dr John Roberts, surgeon, of Bangor, seems to have devoted some attention to the flora of North Wales a century or so ago', and after giving a scant account of the facts which were available then, concludes by saying: 'It would be interesting to know if anyone could supply any further information regarding the subject of this enquiry.'

J.E. Griffith (1843-1933) in the Preface of this *Flora of Anglesey & Carnarvonshire* (1894/5) mentions Dr John Roberts of Bangor as the only person who had taken any interest in the botany of the two counties since the time of the Reverend Hugh Davies, author of *Welsh Botanology* (1813). Griffith goes on to say that Roberts was a personal friend of bryologist William Wilson of Warrington, and that Roberts' herbarium, which he claimed to have seen, contained no Anglesey plants and but few Caernarfonshire ones; these he says were given to him by Wilson. Griffith in his *Flora* erroneously gives 1828 as the

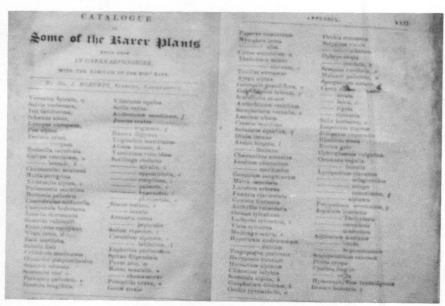

List of Snowdonian plants by John Roberts.

92

year of Roberts' death, but the correct date of 1849 appears in his much acclaimed *Pedigrees of Anglesey and Carnarvonshire Families* published in 1914.

According to Griffith (1914) page 332 John Roberts was the son of Caernarfon blacksmith Robert Jones of Pen y clip who died 18 May 1829 aged 64. The children of Robert Jones and his wife Elizabeth are named as follows: Dr John Roberts of Bangor, William Roberts Jones, Robert Roberts, a smith at Caernarfon, Ann who married Rice Owen a chemist, of Pwllheli, and Elizabeth who married Richard Griffith, a saddler at Bangor. An entry in the Llanbeblig Parish Register shows that 'John Roberts Son of Robert Jones, Smith by Elizabeth' was christened on 28 September 1792. An interesting note on the same subject is that given by John Wynne on page 49 of his book *Sir a Thref Caernarfon fel yr oeddynt ac fel y maent yn 1860* (County and Town of Caernarfon as it used to be and as it is in 1860). Wynne claims that Dr John Roberts of Bangor was the son of Robert Jones, a blacksmith, of Penymaes, Caernarfon. There can be little doubt that both Griffith and Wynne are dealing with the same family, except the latter has Penymaes as opposed to the former's Pen y clip.

John Roberts served his apprenticeship at the Caernarvonshire and Anglesey Loyal Dispensary, which had been opened in October 1810; he was probably articled to Dr James Roose who was apothecary and secretary in 1813. Roberts later succeeded Roose in this position and he was appointed house surgeon in November 1818. Also attending the Loyal Dispensary during this period were the surgeons Thomas Roberts and Rice Griffith, and physician William Mason, a graduate of Edinburgh University, who was appointed in 1812. A year following his appointment as house surgeon, Roberts resigned his position announcing his intention through the press of opening a practice at Caernarfon.

During his time at the Bangor Dispensary he became known to the Reverend Hugh Davies, but apart from being advised on the proper books on botany and the method of study he gained but little advantage from this acquaintance which was terminated by Davies' death in 1821. John Roberts however, despite his announcement of moving to Caernarfon and despite the fact that Bailey Williams describes him as 'Mr J. Roberts, Surgeon, Caernarvon' in the heading of the catalogue of plants which Roberts contributed to his *Tourist's Guide &c* (1821), remained in Bangor.

A John Roberts of Bangor took his membership examination at the Royal College of Surgeons of England, Lincoln's Inn, on 2 July 1824. The *Medical Directory*, first published in 1845, lists John Roberts as an apothecary before 1815 and a surgeon in 1824. He practised at Castle Street; (now the lower section of the Bangor High Street) at number 315 on the corner of High Street and Dean Street, which was for many years the premises of Thomas Lewis & Co, a grocer's shop.

John Roberts married Jane, the daughter of Elias Jones of Gorswen, and of The Abbey, near Llanrwst and his wife Jane, daughter of Richard Evans of Llwydfaen. They had five children, Elias John, Jane, Robert, John and Elizabeth. Roberts' wife Jane died in 1835, and in a letter to William Wilson of Warrington dated 27 December, he acknowledges the latter's letter of sympathy. Jane Roberts during that year had, as usual, been managing the domestic affairs of their farm, and had bought a plot of land at Garth, on the northern outskirts of the city, where she was busy supervising the building of a cottage. She caught a cold at the cottage on 7 November, and as her condition worsened with headaches and fever she took to her bed on the 20th and died soon after. It is not known if Roberts ever took up residence at the new cottage following his wife's death, nor are there any further facts known to the writer concerning the farm which is mentioned in the letter.

Among the correspondence of William Wilson at the Central Library, Warrington are six letters in the hand of John Roberts; these have been addressed from Bangor. Botany is the prime subject of discussion in these letters, but they also reveal matters which are of a very personal nature (which will be discussed later) and this proves that the two men were close friends. According to his notice in *The Lancet* (vol i, 1849) Roberts by 1820 had formed a considerable collection of dried plants which he had gathered on Snowdon, Glyder and the districts around Bangor. This is inconsistent with Griffith (1894/5) who states that Roberts' herbarium contained 'but few Carnarvonshire' plants. One can therefore but assume that the earlier herbarium was either dispersed or became lost or destroyed before Griffith's time. He availed himself of the opportunity to gather this collection of plants while visiting patients who lived in the mountain districts.

A number of very eminent English botanists came to stay with him in Bangor, and he used to accompany them on excursions to Cwm Idwal, Snowdon and parts of Anglesey to look for plants. During one of these botanical excursions led by Roberts the Snowdon lily (*Lloydia serotina*) was rediscovered on the rocks of the Devil's Kitchen above Cwm Idwal. It was believed that since the time of John Wynne Griffith of Garn (mentioned earlier) this plant had been gathered by no other botanist from this particular site, and the fact of its growing there had become merely traditional. It should be pointed out, however, that secrecy has always played a major part in field botany, especially during the period under discussion when the over collecting of plants from a site could (and did) lead to the extermination of a rare species.

Most botanists kept their knowledge of rare plant localities to themselves and would only share that knowledge with those whom they trusted. Owen Rowlands of Blaen y nant (1742-1817), a skilful bone-setter and botanist, knew well the '*Lloydia*' site on the Devil's Kitchen cliffs, but kept the locality secret despite constant badgering from plant collectors. He finally divulged his long cherished secret on his death bed.   Roberts undertook a botanical ramble on 19 June 1844 in the company of Joseph Sidebotham (1824-1885) of Manchester, (one of the founders of that city's Field Naturalists Society) an account of which was published by the visitor in *The Phytologist*. Following a short stay at Beaumaris, Sidebotham had previously made an excursion through Bangor, and along the Holyhead Road to Llyn Ogwen, and from there into Cwm Idwal, the Devil's Kitchen and crossing the mountain from Llyn y Cŵn down into Llanberis. On the following day he ascended Snowdon and inspected the slate quarries on his return. During this visit he was unsuccessful in his main object, since he failed to procure a specimen of the Snowdon lily (*Lloydia serotina*).

John Roberts joined Sidebotham at Bangor on his second visit and they took a conveyance as far as the Penrhyn slate quarries where one of the quarrymen joined them, bringing a rope as had been previously arranged by Roberts. The group then continued on to Cwm Idwal, skirting the lake and observing water lobelia (*Lobelia dortmanna*), quillwort (*Isoetes lacustris*) and awlwort (*Subularia aquatica*) on the way. Rain began to fall heavily as they ascended the rocky slopes to the base of the Devil's Kitchen chasm and from there up the steep 'Llwybr y carw' (the deer path) which emerges on a plateau a short distance from Llyn y Cŵn. The following plants were recorded from the cliffs above the path: globeflower (*Trollius europaeus*), alpine meadow-rue (*Thalictrum alpinum*), roseroot (*Sedum rosea*) spring sandwort (*Minuartia verna*), mountain everlasting (*Antennaria dioica*), and a saxifrage whose identity caused uncertainty and which Sidebotham records as 'I suppose to be S.*caespitosa*'. This, the tufted saxifrage, is among the plants which Roberts listed for Bailey Williams' *Tourist Guide* (1821) and gives the locality as 'near Twll Du'.

On arriving at the top of the Devil's Kitchen chasm the quarryman was lowered by rope down the face of the cliff to the spot where several flowers of the Snowdon lily (*Lloydia serotina*) had been spotted, but climbed back soon after, saying that the rope was too short to reach them. At this point in his account of the incident Sidebotham remarks 'I had to act as guide, being the only one of the party who had visited the place before'. This was not so, as the list of plants which appeared in Bailey Williams' *Tourist's Guide* of 1821 show that Roberts was well acquainted with the Devil's Kitchen, and indeed the whole of the Snowdonian range for a period of at least 24 years prior to Sidebotham's visit. The party then moved to a lower step which was closer to the *Lloydia* site and from this point John Roberts, after securing the rope around his waist, while the others held fast to the other end at the top, lowered himself down the face of the cliff. He reappeared a few minutes later with a few specimens held in his mouth and more in his hat. By this time, the mist which had hung low over the mountain was now beginning to clear, and the botanists next walked in the direction of Glyder Fawr to search for the oblong woodsia

(*Woodsia ilvensis*), a very rare fern. In this they were unsuccessful as the rock on which the oblong woodsia (*Woodsia ilvensis*) grew was found to be completely devoid of the plant. The '*Woodsia*' site near Llyn y Cŵn was well known to Roberts and he had on previous occasions led other botanists there. Sussex botanist William Borrer (1781-1862) is said to have 'gathered it in plenty'. Borrer's letter to William Wilson requesting assistance to procure certain specimens from Snowdonia and Anglesey is dated 19 May 1834, and is a fine example of the badgering to which the Snowdonian botanists were subjected during the 19th century: ' . . . obliged if you can give me such directions as may enable me to find readily some of the rarest plants of which I engage to help myself so moderately as not to endanger their extermination. *W.ilvensis*, most anxious to find, *Sax caespitosa, Anthericum serotinum*, at Snowdon, *Rosa wilsonii* at Bangor. In Anglesey — *Knappia agrostilea Lysimachia thyrsiflora A.guttatus, Brassica monensis, Elatine hydropiper, Potam. lanceolata, Alisma ranunculoides, A. natans, Callitriche autumnalis . . . '

Another fern of the same family, and of equal rarity in Snowdonia, the alpine woodsia (*Woodsia alpina*) seems to have suffered the same fate. G.W. Francis (1800-1865) in his book *An Analysis of the British Ferns* (1837) quotes C.C. Babington on page 27 of the fourth edition 1851: 'I was not able to find this plant on Glyd[e]r Fawr, Caernarvonshire, July 1835 although in company with J. Roberts, Esq., of Bangor, who knew its station well. It is, I fear, exterminated in that place. I searched for it in the same spot in 1837 and a botanical friend in 1840 but both without success.'

Another interesting note which testifies to the collecting of plants from the Cwm Idwal area appears in Hugh Derfel Hughes' *Antiquities of Llandegai and Llanllechid* (1866). It refers to 'John Roberts Penclip' and other local doctors such as O.O. Roberts of Bangor, O. Rowland, Blaen Nant and John Owen, Pant y Ffrydlas, who visited the Devil's Kitchen cliffs every year armed with ropes and long sticks with small hooks attached which were used to uproot the plants they could not reach.

Some of the letters Roberts sent to Wilson contain family news and current affairs, and as would be expected from two of congenial spirit, botanical matters. In one letter the medical man advises Wilson to bring his ailing mother to Wales for a holiday during the months of May or June, to drink plenty of buttermilk; he was quite convinced that her complaint was purely 'fanciful'. The subject then changes to plants, and a botanical excursion is planned. 'If you can reach only Ormshead in May pray let me know of your arrival.' In another letter Roberts urges Wilson to take more physical exercise to combat his varicose veins, which were 'the result of sedentary life causing languid circulation . . . you ought to use as much exercise as you can daily without fatiguing yourself.' In a letter dated 15 July 1833 Roberts expresses deep relief that the cholera epidemic did not reach the city of Bangor. 'It was if

Purple saxifrage
(Saxifraga oppositifolia)

Oblong woodsia
(Woodsia ilvensis)

Tufted saxifrage
(Saxifraga cespitosa)

Killarney fern
(Trichomanes speciosum)

Dwarf willow
(Salix herbacea)

Moss campion
(Silene acaulis)

Roseroot
(Sedum rosea)

Alpine bistort
(Persicaria vivipara)

Alpine saxifrage
(Saxifraga nivalis)

Snowdon lily
(Lloydia serotina)

Mountain avens
(Dryas octopetala)

Alpine cinquefoil
(Potentilla crantzii)

not singular that we were most mercifully exempted from the ravages of Cholera, not a single case occured in Bangor although it raged at Beaumaris & Caernarvon to both which places I went to see several cases — I am much obliged for your communication respecting Mr Hale's treatment, but I am convinced of what is now the opinion of the most eminent & candid Physicians that more cases would have done well if left to nature and cold water than under any other treatment whatsoever, no doubt many were killed by experiments; & bleeding in the stage of collapse would prove instantatiously fatal, indeed the blood will not flow in that stage, the best plan is to say that we know nothing at all about it, at least respecting the cure of it — that is my firm opinion —'.

In the same letter Roberts thanks Wilson for sending him a copy of 'Mr Winch's Flora'. Nathaniel John Winch (1768-1838) was secretary at the Newcastle Infirmary and with J. Thornhill and R. Waugh was co-author of the *Botanist's Guide through . . . Northumberland and Durham* published in two volumes between 1805 and 1807. He also wrote the *Essay on Geographical Distribution of Plants . . . of Northumberland, Cumberland and Durham*, 1819 with a second edition appearing in 1825, and *Remarks on Flora Cumberland*, also in 1825. Roberts' letter could refer to any of these, and remarks, 'the old boy must have taken a good deal of trouble to put it together — the Cryptogamic portion is all Chinese to me further than the *Jungermanniae . . .*' He then goes on to say how his work at certain times restricted his botanical rambles to the Bangor district, ' . . . indeed I am now more completely tied down & confined to certain limits than ever I was before, in consequence of having so many midwifery cases upon hand. If I go far, the Ladies in this country are not always so accommodating as wait my return.'

Another correspondent and friend of John Roberts was John Eddowes Bowman (1785-1841) whose chief interests were mosses, fungi and later geology. One letter records the visit to Wales of two of Bowman's sons, who came primarily to see Telford's bridge across the Menai Straits; the letter, which was delivered to Roberts by the young men mentions a visit made by Bowman and another botanist to the Devil's Kitchen a month previously with a view to collecting specimens of the Snowdon lily (*Lloydia serotina*), when they failed to find a single plant. Roberts then says that he received a note a little before then from a Mr Trimmer who resided at Caernarfon which also contained a fern specimen that he would like Roberts to identify for him. 'It proved to be the *Asplenium septentrionale* [forked spleenwort] at the same time of gathering it, he says that he found *[A]nthericum* [Snowdon lily] in flower having procured them with ropes to let down to the side of Twlldu chasm. I am afraid we shall not be able to get any in future without having recourse to the same plan.' It was evident from comments such as this that the rare plants of Snowdonia were at this time being collected to the point where none were being left for others. The first plant collector to arrive at any rare plant site would pick all the plants he could reach. None was spared; the acquiring of a complete herbarium was paramount.

The latest botanical publications, gossip, and domestic news were discussed in the letters, and Roberts relied on Wilson for information regarding the former. 'I shall thank you much to write me [Roberts to Wilson] a few lines to say how you are getting on — what news from the botanical world, how your mother and brother are . . . I still take the Magazine of Natl History & Hookers Miscellany. Pray what kind of Book is the new Edition of the English Flora published by Sowerby. I was at Llanbedrog in Lleyn lately seeing an old gentleman Dr Williams, and near the house on the sandy coast I could find quantity of an *'Euphorbia'* [spurge] which I was not acquainted with, it proves to be the *E.Paralia &* and I see that Davies y dail mentions his having found it there in abundance. Did you ask Dr Hooker respecting his 'System of Plants' whether it ever was published. I shall feel very much obliged if you could at some future period lend me Arnott's botanical article in the new edition of Napier's Encyclopaedia, for I think from what they say, that the perusal of it would give me much pleasure. I understand that you are very busy arranging Drummond's mosses, which you mention, he gathered on the Missouri, New Orleans etc . . . . are there many of these mosses similar to my N. American ones or are they all new & different ones, if they are mostly new and different to mine I should like to buy a set to make my flora more complete — i.e. if they will be sold in packets, like the others.'

The fate of Roberts' collection of mosses is not known to the writer. The herbarium of the National Museum of Wales, Cardiff contains a mere two vascular plants and one moss collected by Roberts. The vascular plants are both mossy saxifrage (*Saxifraga hypnoides*) and the label reads 'Col. Dr John Roberts, Twll Du 1828'. The second specimen being identical with the addition of the month (7) to the date.

John Roberts' interest in botany continued to the last and during the latter part of his life he also became interested in the science of geology. His notice in *The Lancet* and *Carnarvon Herald* states: 'The contemplation of the works of nature was doubtless a solace to him during many a gloomy hour,' and these 'gloomy' periods could well refer to his experiences following the death of his wife Jane in December 1835. The death is not recorded in the *Pedigrees* (1914) of J.E. Griffith and neither is the later marriage of John Roberts to his second wife.

The identity of his second wife remains unknown; all that is known of her background is the fact that her father lived at Liverpool. The whole incident concerning the second marriage would have remained unknown had it not been for a letter which Roberts had written to William Wilson of Warrington on 7 January 1844. The letter mentions a visit to Bangor made by William Wilson and his wife earlier that year during which time Mrs Wilson was expecting a baby. John Roberts apologises for the behaviour of his wife, who by the time of writing had gone back to Liverpool. 'I was surely afraid that the disturbance which Mrs R. created that night would have had some bad effect, however I hope not'. Details of what happened on the night in question are not given, but there is no question that the relationship between the botanist and his second wife had been intolerable for some time. ' . . . Mrs Jezebel is gone to Liverpool and has been there about 3 months & is likely to be there a long time as she has brought me into difficulties out of which I cannot easily extricate myself . . . for unless my wife reforms I am determined to keep her with her father until she does, for otherwise I shall never put up with her nor live with her for I would rather live like an old batchelor & keep Jane as a housekeeper, than to be in continual trouble and anxiety with a woman (when too much excited) is callous to every reason & all feelings of decency & morality.' Despite being troubled with personal and domestic problems, Roberts nevertheless finds the time and the will to indulge in his hobby and carry out his duties as a doctor. 'I sent the plants to Mr Edwards. It is not improbable but I shall take a trip to see you this Spring as I expect I must go to London upon some Lunacy business.'

The last of his letters known to the writer is dated 24 January 1844, and in this also the strong attachment to botany is seen to overcome his many predicaments. Wilson, who before his early retirement had been a practising solicitor, informed Roberts of his intention to write a strongly worded letter to Mrs Roberts, still at Liverpool, regarding the incident at Bangor during which Mrs Wilson, being then pregnant had appeared to have been upset. The letter however was not sent. 'I was glad' writes Roberts, 'you did not write as you once intended for it would only aggrevate certain kinds of inflammatory feelings & passions without mending them & it would indeed be only throwing pearls before a swine — hwch. I was very glad to hear that Mrs Wilson is gradually recovering her strength & sorry to hear that the baby's strength is such a precarious state. Mrs R. is still in Liverpool but I expect she will be returning here in about a fortnight. Your Uncle's motto was a good one 'what cannot be cured must be endured'. I certainly have had that self-possession and strength of mind to bear all the evils I am beset with, with more courage & *equo animo* than I expected considering all circumstances.'

Botany then takes over in the form of a discussion on a volume entitled *Flora Italicae*, which according to Roberts contained the most correct account 'as well as the most minute in Latin of not only the *Callitriches*, but of all other plants which he describes.' He also points out that Wilson's name appears in the text concerning the taxonomy of certain mosses. In reply to a previous request from Wilson Roberts assures the bryologist that he will gather the mosses from the Bangor area for him. 'I shall gather the Hypnum in the Canal near the Baths — *Hypnum fluviatile* near the Cegin catteracts and also

Jungermannia viticulosa I shall get up an hour earlier in order to procure them.'
He concludes the letter by saying 'I hope as you say that I shall find my
domestic affairs in future more comfortable and that my mind will be more at
ease — however I feel very happy even now in my own mind.'

John Roberts died on 27 April 1849 at Bangor and was buried in the
Cathedral graveyard; his gravestone lies by the side of the pathway which
connects Glanrafon Hill with Ffordd Gwynedd.

John Williams and the *Faunula Grustensis*

'It is ridiculous in a man to travel for improvement, while he remains ignorant of those things that are about him at home.' So wrote John Williams (1801-1859) on the title page of his book *Faunula Grustensis* published in 1830. This volume, neatly printed by John Jones at Llanrwst, is unusual in that it is a catalogue listing all birds, animals and plants to be found in the parish of Llanrwst; most other such works dealt with counties. The book is dedicated to John Wynne Griffith of Garn who, Williams writes, 'in his younger days explored the productions of all the mountains and valleys in North Wales, and therefore he is acquainted with the habitats of the rare Plants.'

John Williams was born in Llansantffraid Glan Conwy on 1 March 1801, the son of Cadwaladr Williams of Eidda Fawr, Ysbyty Ifan, and Jane Williams who hailed from Dolwyddelan. They resided at the mill house at Felin Ucha, Pentrefelin where Cadwaladr Williams worked as a miller, and he, being a cultured man with a keen interest in literature ensured that his eight children were educated, initially at home, and later in the Sunday School.

Cadwaladr and Jane Williams were members at the Methodist Chapel in Llansantffraid Glan Conwy, and Cadwaladr Williams was instrumental in establishing the first Sunday School in Llandudno. During those days flour could not be bought in Llandudno, only wheat, and during the summer when the wind was not sufficiently strong to turn the windmill near Glanwydden, the wheat was carted to the water powered mills at Llansantffraid, and in dry summers over Tal y cafn to the mills at Talybont and Borthllwyd near Trefriw. Cadwaladr Williams, being concerned at the level of illiteracy among the young men who drove the wheat carts to his mill from Llandudno suggested to his fellow Methodists the idea of starting a Sunday School in that village. A certain James Williams and W. Davies of Llandudno then joined in the venture with the people of Llansantffraid in procuring the use of the barn of Peter Jones, Pwll y Gwichiaid as a schoolroom. Two or three people walked six or seven miles from Llansantffraid to teach at the school which opened in the year 1806.

When eleven years of age John Williams, together with his older brother William, spent a year in Liverpool attending the Harrington Academy at Bradford Place, Toxteth Park, their ambition during this time being aimed towards a career at sea. In addition to maritime lessons the brothers were also taught mathematics, keeping accounts and English grammar. The romance of the sea soon faded however and at the end of that year the brothers returned home to help their father at the mill. William was later apprenticed to a chemist and surgeon, studied at London and Dublin, and obtained a licence to operate as a chemist and surgeon at Abergele. He died when thirty-seven years of age on 11 June 1834, but the shop was kept by his widow Mary until her death in 1873.

According to Thomas Shankland, writing in *Ceninen Gŵyl Ddewi* (1916), John Williams spent a term as an apprentice gardener on one of the large estates in the Conwy valley, but precisely which one is not known. James

Faunula Grustensis:

BEING AN OUTLINE OF THE

NATURAL CONTENTS

OF THE

PARISH OF LLANRWST;

Comprehending some account of its

GENERAL HISTORY,

COMMERCE AND AGRICULTURE;

ALSO,

A Triglott Catalogue

(In Latin, English, and Welsh)

OF THE ANIMALS AND PLANTS FOUND IN IT,
WITH SOME NOTES THEREON;

TO WHICH IS ADDED,

A Rudimental view of its Chemistry;

AND A CATALOGUE

(In Latin, English, and Welsh)

OF THE

Diseases that have occurred therein.

BY JOHN WILLIAMS.

It is ridiculous in a man to travel for improvement, while he
remains ignorant of those things that are about him at home.

"Hic patet ingeniis campus."

Llanrwst:

PRINTED BY JOHN JONES.
1830.

Britten (*Journal of Botany vol.x/viii*) notes that he worked as a gardener for the Countess of Bridgewater at Ashridge, Hertsfordshire between the years 1823 and 1827. Here he was permitted the use of the library and among the collection was a copy of *Hortus Gramineus Woburnensis* by George Sinclair (1786-1834), who was once gardener to the Duke of Bedford. The book was published privately in 1816 and contained dried specimens of grasses carefully arranged and labelled. John Williams spent a further three years at Kew Gardens and the Chelsea Physic Garden, then under the curatorship of William Anderson (1766-1846). His younger brother Moses was apprenticed to become an apothecary at Abergele under the care of the eldest brother William, and after five years went up to London in 1824 at the age of twenty-one. Moses trained for six months at St Thomas Hospital qualifying for his Licenciateship of the Society of Apothecaries (L.S.A.) on 13 December 1827. Licenciateships were granted only to persons who had completed a course of training. He returned to Wales and practised at Abergele, Rhuddlan and St Asaph, and is referred to as a 'surgeon' in the trade directory of 1828 while his brother William is described as a 'druggist and grocer'.

There is no definite evidence that John Williams was granted the L.S.A., but Thomas Shankland, writing in *Ceninen Gŵyl Ddewi* (1916), page 42, is of the opinion that he did. He left London in 1827 and was apprenticed to his brother William at Abergele and according to his own testimony he was a practising doctor at Llanrwst by 1830. An article which was written by the Reverend John Williams, son of the John Williams in question, and appeared in *Bye-gones*, 22 November 1893, reveals that the physician obtained his M.D. at the Royal College of Surgeons, Dublin under the tuition of the doctors Robert Harrison, Arthur Jacob and Samuel Stretten. The name John Williams appears in the *Examiners Book* 1817-1837 registered as one of Mr Harrison's pupils on 24 January 1832, but there is no record of either of the brothers in the minutes of the Court of Examiners 1817-1837 and these facts cause much uncertainty concerning the training of John Williams.

He took a great deal of interest in agriculture as well as botany; these interests no doubt arose from the influence of his greatly admired acquaintance John Wynne Griffith of Garn (1763-1834), mentioned earlier. He subscribed to the Royal Agricultural Society's journal and during 1842 submitted an essay entitled 'The Food of Plants' in response to a competition that the society had arranged. His entry proved unsuccessful and it was not printed in the journal, but the composition shows that he was highly talented and possessed a great deal of knowledge on plant science. The essay also points out various means by which the farmer could improve his land, a matter on which John Wynne Griffith had spoken strongly in favour during his period as an M.P. John Williams urged farmers to experiment with several strips of land set aside for the purpose, leaving one strip untreated and applying various types of fertilizer to the others. They should then plant a variety of vegetables in each plot which would in due course show the farmer which fertilizer was best suited to each vegetable. He goes on to suggest that farmers would benefit from learning the principles of chemistry, zoology and botany and he was also in favour of establishing agricultural schools throughout the country, or an agricultural department in every school. This, he writes, would improve and prepare those pupils whose aim in life was to become capable and efficient farmers. He wrote several letters to the *Medical Times*, the first, which was written on 23 April 1843, appeared under the heading 'Observations on the Spleen' and was signed 'Corvenius'. The second letter was dated 15 August 1843 giving his own opinions on the 'Law of Periodicity' regarding the disagreement between the doctors Laycock and Dickson. This letter was signed 'Cymro'. He again wrote to the *Medical Times* on 3 January 1844 in support of comments made by a certain Mr Yeatman concerning mercury, and again on 24 September discussing dropsy. The last letter was undersigned by his own name, but he used the pseudonym 'Corvenius' again when discussing the professional standards of doctors. On 7 August 1844 the bill of Sir James Graham entitled *Further regulation of the Profession of Physic and Surgery* underwent its first reading in the House of Commons. This bill was aimed at improving the professional standards of doctors and so control the numbers of unqualified 'doctors' who operated freely during those days. The bill received its second reading on 28 February 1845, but despite the fact that it was approved by the House and discussed by the Select Committee it never became law due to widespread disagreement and bad feeling between the various medical reformers. John Williams was of the opinion that the new measure, if it became law, would mean 'allowing every mercenary and ignorant empiric to practise'. This sentence confirms that he himself was a licenced doctor; an unqualified 'quack' would hardly express himself in such a manner to the readers of the *Medical Times*.

During the years 1829 and 1830, while living at Llanrwst, John Williams began to study and collate his researches into the natural history of the parish; a work which culminated in the publication of his book *Faunula Grustensis*. He begins the book with the following words: 'My principal motive in compiling this treatise was to give a Catalogue of the Animals, Plants, Minerals, &c. which this parish contains, so that we might have some idea of what is, and what is not to be found in it: but as this itself would have been dry and uninteresting to many, I have endeavoured to collect as many facts relating to its general history, commerce, agriculture, &c. as would become the limits allotted to my little Fauna.' He names Sir John Wynn's *History of the Gwydir Family*, and Thomas Pennant's *Tours in Wales* as being the main sources of his 'general observations'. He also pays tribute to Edward Lhuyd, Hugh Davies and John Wynne Griffith when referring to the field of natural history. He also mentions 'the natural genius for plants of Richard Roberts of Melin y Coed', who will be mentioned again later.

The preface of the book concludes with a few remarks which show his concern at the lack of similar books published in Wales on natural history. Reading, he says was very popular among the Welsh, but the great majority of books dealt with theology and poetry. The *Faunula Grustensis*, he hoped, would encourage more studies in the Sciences, as well as the Arts. There were at the time several Botanic Gardens, as well as Schools of Medicine in England and Ireland, but none in Wales, and John Williams voiced his concern over this by stating, 'how can she [Wales] nurture her geniuses?'

In describing the Nant Bwlch yr Heyrn district John Williams names the plants for which this area is famous: the alpine penny-cress (*Thlaspi caerulescens*) on the authority of J.W. Griffith is reported as growing 'abundantly near the Cataract'; bog-myrtle (*Myrica gale*) abundant and perfumes the air with its spicy smell. In summer branches of this plant are taken and laid between the bed clothes to drive away fleas.'

The 'Murddun' or ruins of the house of Taliesin, the sixth century bard is according to the *Faunula* 'still to be seen about 300 yards this side' of Llyn Geirionnydd, and the surrounding district is described as being barren and 'consisting of Heaths and Bogs, but lately, Lord Willoughbyde Eresby has planted several thousands of trees, so that in few years it will be much more valuable than it has been, since the great arboreal desolation.'

Capel Curig is unique in that it has 'an extraordinary large Inn' and the lakes Llynnau Mymbyr were much frequented by anglers; the Welsh poppy (*Meconopsis cambrica*), globeflower (*Trollius europaeus*), water lobelia (*Lobelia dortmanna*), awlwort (*Subularia aquatica*), quillwort (*Isoetes*) and the ivy-leaved bellflower (*Wahlenbergia hederacea*) are the plants noted around the Capel Curig area. The 'extraordinary large Inn' referred to earlier was the hotel built by Lord Penrhyn shortly after 1800, now the centre for outdoor activities called Plas y Brenin.

The summit ridge of Moel Siabod, being the furthest border on the eastern side of the parish of Llanrwst is named as having the finest view of the Snowdon group of mountains and notes the following plants as growing on Moel Siabod: alpine saxifrage (*Saxifraga nivalis*), starry saxifrage (*Saxifraga stellaris*), mossy saxifrage (*Saxifraga hypnoides*), and the club-mosses *Diphasiastrum alpinum*, *Huperzia selago*, and *Selaginella selaginoides*. The ring ouzel is noted as a regular visitor during the season.

Pennant's account of the view from the summit of Snowdon is quoted in its entirety followed by an extensive list of rare plants for which the region is noted. From Moel Siabod the parish boundaries are followed towards Betws-y-coed where Pennant is quoted as saying 'the noblest oaks in all Wales grew on this rock, within memory of man'. Williams goes on; 'I remember the stools of several which proved they were equal to any which flourish in the deepest soil; yet these rocks are totally destitute of earth for a considerable way'. Williams was always a keen advocate of the planting of trees, and adds 'I have no doubt the Fir and other hardy trees would grow on the summit of Snowdon, for trees are found to grow in much colder countries than Snowdon is; instance Sweden, Norway . . . ' John Wynn of Gwydir writing of an earlier period states that 'the countrey of Nantconway was not only wooded, but also all Carnarvon, Meirioneth, and Denbigh shires seemed to be but one continued forrest, having few inhabitants, though of all other Nantconway had the fewest, being the worst then and the seat of the warres, to whom the countrey paid contribution.'

Maenan is mentioned as having a good greenhouse and garden where the evergreen oaks (*Quercus ilex*) adorned the front of the house, and an abundance of spurge-laurel (*Daphne laureola*) grew in a wood by the road. In a nearby plantation John Williams records the deadly nightshade (*Atropa belladonna*) as growing plentifully, and goes on to note the similarities between Maenan and Ashridge in Hertsfordshire where he worked as a gardener between the years 1823 and 1827. Maenan, before the dissolution of the monastries had been an abbey, having been removed there from Conwy in 1289, and Ashridge was formerly a convent. Williams recalls having seen the deadly nightshade there also. John Wynne Griffith of Garn has also observed this plant growing near three or four abbeys in North Wales and Williams suggests that the monks must have used it as a rat poison, to provide the 'effects of holy embraces'. It was used by the common people of the neighbourhood to ease pain from swellings of the legs and also for rheumatism.

John Williams' keen eye for plants becomes evident even when he writes about the town and castle of Conwy as he adds the odd botanical note to the text. 'Near Porth ucha' the *Rubia peregrina* [wild madder] grows so luxuriant as to be scarcely cognizable. The *Dianthus Caryophyllus* [clove pink] plentiful on the walls'. J.E. Griffith, who wrote *The Flora of Anglesey and Carnarvonshire* (1894/5) has no record of wild madder (*Rubia peregrina*) from Conwy, and the only species of the Dianthus genus to be recorded by him from the town walls of Conwy was the pink (*Dianthus plumaris*). 'On Conway Town walls N. side!' The extensive salt marsh tract at Conwy belonged to the Corporation of the town during Williams' day, and large mounds of muscle shells, left there by the pearl gatherers, were piled at one end, Conwy pearls being considered equal to any in Britain. Plants such as the sea bindweed (*Calystegia soldanella*), field gentian (*Gentianella campestris*), sea rocket (*Cakile maritima*) (which Griffith also recorded in his *Flora*) (1894/5), and bloody crane's-bill (*Geranium sanguineum*) were noted from the area.

The areas including Pen y gogarth, or Great Orme's Head and Bodysgallen have always been a favourite hunting ground for botanists and Williams proudly attributes the finding of the wild cotoneaster (*Cotoneaster cambricus*) to his esteemed friend John Wynne Griffith of Garn. Griffith first found the plant in 1783 but failed to communicate a specimen to Sir J.E. Smith who at the time was collating information for inclusion in his *English Botany*. There follows a short list of all the plants found in the Llandudno area.

The commerce and agriculture of the parish is dealt with next; the crops which were grown during Williams' time are noted together with sound advice to farmers on how to improve the land for a better yield. 'The encouraging of Agriculture and Industry would give a new face to the country: it would ignite a more general spirit of enquiry, and make us know the great importance of diligence and exertion'. The corn-sellers who attended the weekly market at Llanrwst came from nearby Eglwysfach, Llansantffraid, Creuddyn, Llandrillo and Abergele, while the buyers came from further afield: Beddgelert, Ffestiniog, Llangwm, Cerrig y Drudion and Penmachno. In the mountainous regions only oats, barley and potatoes were grown, and the farmers relied on selling cattle to the English markets for money.

John Williams was in favour of the commercialisation and expansion of the textile industry in the Conwy Valley. 'Could not the Flax be brought to a more general cultivation?' he asks. He was of the opinion that flax would grow on any kind of land and that every part of the plant would be put to some use: linseed oil could be had from the seed, and the remaining substance (the linseed cake) would provide 'a wholesome food for cattle'. The straw would then be used in the manufacturing of linen: 'could we not manufacture this as well as wool, and obtain a large quantity of good linen and flannel of our own growth and produce . . . . ' He foresaw the industrialisation of the Conwy Valley as being able to compete favourably with the mills of Lancashire. 'If our river, vale, and water power, had been near the active and spirited manufacturers of Manchester, it would have been universally allowed to be equal to any place in the world for conveniency, with respect to water-power for looms, and the river for exportation'.

He recommended the planting of fruit trees and called for an increase in the number of orchards, stating that only one or two had been planted in the parish over the past fifty years. Apples and cider would help to pay the rent of a farm and he argues that much money is made in Herefordshire out of their apple trees. 'We cannot expect to ripen grapes and make wine in Wales as they do in France; . . . [but] . . . no one would deny that Cyder and Perry could be produced here as well as in any other part of the world'. Another of his proposals was the making and exporting of a 'celebrated Llanrwst Ale'. The hop, being a hardy plant, which grew abundantly in the hedges of the parish, could be planted for commercial purposes in specially cultivated plots. 'Many Noblemen, &c. in England have their Hop garden on their own Farms. We can be no more justified in sending to England for Hops than we should if we were sending thither for malt'. John Williams was a strong advocate of self

107

sufficiency; his ideals cover almost all aspects of agriculture and industry and he was always ready to encourage improvement in the use of land and the introduction of new agrarian techniques.

The catalogue of animals and plants indigenous to the parish of Llanrwst which appear in the *Faunula Grustensis* was the result of a single season's field work by the author. Several additional records are inserted on the authority of John Wynne Griffith of Garn, Thomas Pennant and Richard Roberts of Melin y coed. The whole class of cryptogammic plants, excluding the ferns, were omitted. John Williams encourages others to observe and record the native flora of their surrounding communities. 'Any one might with a little trouble, collect all the native plants in this neighbourhood, although perhaps, this would not be in itself of great importance, but as a part of Science it would be very commendable. I have myself collected above 5,000 different species of plants, Indigenous and Exotic'.

The botanical section of the catalogue lists 532 plants between pages 80 and 118 followed by a further 22 pages containing a list of garden plants. The book concludes with notes on chemistry and nosology (the classification of diseases). Some very interesting and informative notes have been appended to some plant names; they regard mainly the localities where the plant in question grows or its medicinal qualities. The bogbean (*Menyanthes trifoliata*), whose infusion is recommended as a tonic, is extremely bitter, and a 'diaretic and purgative; useful in dropsy and rheumatism: sometimes used instead of hops, 2oz of these being equal to a pound of Hops'. The berries of the spindle tree (*Euonymus europaeus*) when dried and ground are sprinkled on the hair to destroy lice. John Williams quotes Pennant regarding the lady's bedstraw (*Galium verum*) 'Above Bwlch y Gwynt, and other places'. "The flowers will congulate boiling milk. Boiled in alum water they tinge wool yellow. The roots dye a fine red, not inferior to madder." He also, like other writers of the period who visited North Wales, notes the use of the rush light in the mountainous districts. The pith of the soft-rush (*Juncus effusus*) was used, 'They strip off the rind (leaving about one-fourth of it unstripped, to strengthen it) then they are once immersed in any melted grease, and laid by for use. When they have no rushes at hand, they have another expedient; they take on old rag, which they roll and twist into a hard cord, this they dip in melted grease, which makes a lasting candle'.

The opium poppy (*Papaver somniferum*) was noted by Williams as being a frequent weed in gardens and other cultivated places. Opium was extracted by winding the green capsules until the white juice exuded, which was then dried. The rare fern forked spleenwort (*Asplenium septentrionale*) is still extant in several sites about Gwydir Castle and Nant Bwlch yr Heyrn, yet John Williams had not seen it there for himself; he writes. 'I cannot find this plant; it is inserted upon the authority Mr Ray gives us in his Synopsis; it is something ambiguous, for we have no place near here called Llandethylae; '*In muris antiquis Llan-Dethylae uno circiter milliari a Llanrhoost aquilonem versus'*. The stately royal fern (*Osmunda regalis*) completes the botanical list. 'In the river that flows from Llyn Geirionydd, and above Trefriw, tho' not strictly within this parish'.

On 1 January 1838 John Williams married Emma Owen (1801-1868) at St Hilary's Church, Denbigh; he had been living in Corwen since May 1832 having established a medical practice there. Emma was the youngest of the fourteen children of Thomas Owen (1757-1827), the Rector of Llangelynin, Meirionnydd and Jane Giles (1759-1848) of Rhuthun. The 1841 Census Returns show that John and Emma Williams resided at Crown Street, Corwen and were served by a fourteen year old girl called Margaret Williams. Their first child, Jane Emma was born on 17 February 1843, and on 6 December 1844 their son John was born.

In January 1848 gold was discovered in California and by the following year forty thousand emmigrants had moved into San Francisco lured there by an irresistable desire to 'get rich quick'. John Williams, seized by the 'gold fever', sold his property and practice at Corwen and with his family emigrated to America in 1850. He bought several acres of land near Norristown, Pennsylvania and built a home for his wife and family. The house was named 'Corwen Place'. Once his wife and children had settled down in their new home John Williams set out for the gold fields of California. His aim initially was to establish a medical practice among the gold miners and to venture to do a little prospecting himself whenever an opportunity presented itself. John Williams journeyed to California via Panama, but was cheated and robbed of all his possessions before arriving at that city. The American Consul there helped him continue his journey northwards to San Francisco, and following his arrival there he spent his remaining money on equipment and supplies before embarking on his gold-seeking venture. He spent five months in Chenhollow near Placerville and later bought a fifty dollar 'claim' at Ouseley's Bar near Marysville, but soon realized his mistake; despite repeated efforts he never became rich. The hard life of the gold prospector had taken its toll on John Williams during his year spent among the mountains of northern California, but he never missed an opportunity to study his favourite subject, and made several observations about the plants of the new world. Following repeated attacks of yellow fever he decided to sell his interests in California and Pennsylvania and return to Wales with his family in 1853. He practised medicine for a term in Fron Cysyllte near Llangollen, moving soon after to Wrexham and Mold. He died on 1 November 1859 being buried in the Churchyard at Llanfair Dyffryn Clwyd. His son the Reverend John Williams, Rector of Llanwddyn near Oswestry between 1890 and 1916 presented his father's Herbarium, consisting of 5,000 plants and a copy of the *Faunula Grustensis* to the University of Wales, Bangor in 1902.

Richard Roberts of Melin y coed, and the 'Old Mountain Doctor'

In the preface of his *Faunula Grustensis* John Williams pays tribute to Richard Roberts of Melin y coed, Llanrwst and describes him as 'a natural genius for Plants'. Richard Roberts had noted the habitats of the plants he had observed in the parish in the margins of his personal copy of Withering's *Arrangement of British Plants* and the book later came into the possession of John Williams. Richard Roberts is credited with fifteen plant records in the *Faunula Grustensis;* twelve flowering plants and three ferns. They appear as follows: modern scientific names having been used whenever practicable.

Page 90   Dodder *(Cuscuta epithymum)* 'Between Maes gwyn and Gwytherin'

Page 92   Bladdernut *(Staphylea pinnata)* 'About Melin y coed and Bryn tirion'

Page 94   Rosebay willowherb *(Chamerion angustifolium)* 'In Dol Cwm Lannerch'

Page 94   Cranberry *(Vaccinium oxycoccos)* 'In Cae pella Bryn Ifan, Capel Garmon'

Page 100   Marsh cinquefoil *(Potentilla palustris)* 'In Gwaun Ty'n Twll'

Page 101   Common meadow-rue *(Thalictrum flavum)* 'In Gwydir park, above the Waterfall'

Page 105   Daisy-leaved ladies smock *(Cardamine bellidifolia)* 'By Pistyll gwyn, Nant y goron and Gallt yr efal'. This plant appears listed in Withering's *Arrangement of British Plants* (1796, vol. iii page 577) but J.D. Hooker however, in the *'Appendix of Excluded Species'* of his *Students Flora of the British Isles* (3rd ed. 1884) states that the plant was 'Confounded with a form of *C.hirsuta*', i.e. hairy bitter-cress.

Page 107   Dyer's greenweed *(Genista tinctoria)* 'By the Canal, under Ty'n Twll'.

Page 107   Petty whin *(Genista anglica)* 'At Tybrith Ucha'.

Page 112   Purple helleborine *(Epipactis rubra)* 'In Nant Bwlch y gwynt'. This plant appears in Withering's *Arrangement of British Plants* (1796 vol. ii, pages 42-43) named *'Serapias rubra'* and the following note is appended. 'Mr Ray inserted this on the authority of Pluckenet, who says he received it from Ireland, and Mr Hudson says it grows in thickets on the side of mountains about Clapham and Ingleton, Yorkshire, but its existence as a native of Britain or Ireland is yet very doubtful'. This is now considered to be an error for another species of *Epipactis* or *Cephalanthera*.

Richard Roberts was born in 1744, the son of Robert Pritchard of Ty'n y Fynwent, Llanrwst who died 9 July 1774 aged 67. His mother was Lettice Foulkes of the 'Eagles' Llanrwst who died 22 January 1790 aged 79. On 25 February 1785, when he was 41 years of age Richard Roberts married 25 year old Margaret Pritchard of Llannefydd.

Richard Roberts was a farmer and miller who owned his own farm, Tŷ Ucha, and the mill at Melin-y-coed near Llanrwst. He supported the non-conformists and was one of the two deacons to serve the Methodist denomination in their meeting house at a weaver's workshop in the upper part of the town of Llanrwst in 1770. The first Sunday School was held in 1793 in a barn which belonged to Richard Roberts, and four years later his name appeared in an appeal addressed to the Bishop of St Asaph for a licence to conduct religious services at Melin-y-coed.

'We whose names are hereunto signed being Protestant Dissenters of the Church of England do hereby certify to your Lordship that there is a Dwelling House and the adjoining Yard situate lying and being in the Parish of Llanrwst and County of Denbigh and diocese of St Asaph, called and known by the name of Melyn y Coyd intended to be a place of Divine Worship to Almighty God and consecrated to the service of Almighty God and which we request your Lordship will cause to be duly registered in the Registry of St Asaph and a copy thereof delivered to us according to the Act of Toleration in that case made and provided as witness our hands this 24th day of April in the year of our Lord one thousand seven hundred and ninety seven — signed by us Richard Roberts, John Richard, John Hughes, Hugh Jones'.

At the bottom of the document are the following words,

'Entre'd of Record the fourth day of April 1797 in the Publick Episcopal Registry of Saint Asaph, John Jones (Dep.Regr.)'

Richard Roberts was described as being a man of short build, with a slow, careful and deliberate nature. When called upon to address the congregation, this being one of the duties of the head deacon, he would deliver his address slowly, deliberately, and would continue for fifteen or twenty minutes. An incident later in his life caused him to leave the Methodists and join the Independent denomination. During a dry summer, when the streams of the parish were all but dried up, an unexpected downpour happened one Sunday. Richard Roberts took advantage of the swollen stream to work his mill and was subsequently called before the small brotherhood of the chapel to answer to the serious charge made against him of breaking the Sabbath. He argued his case, stating that the prevailing circumstances justified his actions, but the church disagreed. He remained with the Independent Church for the rest of his life, passing away quietly and suddenly at the end of August 1817 while eating his lunch. He was 73 years of age and lies buried close to the porch of the parish Church at Llanrwst. His wife was buried in the year 1834 aged 74. Richard Roberts' son David Roberts, a surgeon, is also named in the Preface of the *Faunula Grustensis*. He died 9 May 1815 aged 26 and lies buried in the same grave as 'David Roberts Mercht. and Harp Maker Who died at Liverpool June 23 1779 Aged 48 years'; the latter named being a brother of Richard Roberts.

Early in the 19th century David Thomas Jones, a doctor who lived at Hafod yr Esgob, Mynydd Llanllyfni in the Nantlle Valley, translated the *Herbal* of Nicholas Culpepper into Welsh. The translated work is known locally as 'Llyfr yr hen Ddoctor Mynydd'; the book of the old Mountain Doctor, which ran into several editions. His son, of the same name was also a well known herbalist and physician. Their medications, especially those related to children's ailments, were said to be well known not only throughout North Wales, but also in parts of Europe and America. The plants used, being gathered from the surrounding countryside, were transplanted with other herbs into their garden at Hafod yr Esgob. Among the tales of the district is one which tells of how a tramp, earlier this century, came through the village of Nebo and paused to gather a cluster of leaves from the roadside close to Hafod yr Esgob. One of the villagers, on enquiring what he wanted the leaves for, was told that a concoction made from those particular leaves was the best cure for a sore throat.

   High on the south western slope of Garnedd Goch, above Llyn Cwm Dulyn is a spring which, according to local tradition, was frequently used by the 'old Mountain Doctor'. It was called 'Ffynnon Doctor', the Doctor's Spring; those patients who suffered from rheumatism were taken to the spring and treated with the cold water which was considered beneficial to this and other ailments of the body. These days the site of the old spring is overgrown with mosses and other plants, but the stones which were placed to support the banks are still visible. The grave of the two doctors stands in the farthest corner of the Scotch Baptist cemetary at Llanllyfni and is marked with the following inscription on one side:

'David Thomas Jones of Hafod yr Esgob
died July 13 1839 aged 60 years
Also Elizabeth, his wife
died June 14 1849 aged 68 years'

and on the opposite side:

'David Thomas Jones, died May 18 1888 aged 64.
Well known throughout North Wales as an eminent Herbalist and Physician'.

The Searches of Bowman and Wilson

The New Botanist's Guide to the Localities of the rarer Plants of Britain (vol.i,1835) by Hewett Cottrell Watson (1804-1881) followed the same pattern as the first published *Botanist's Guide* of Turner and Dillwyn in 1805. Both works listed British plants on a county by county basis, and Watson's first book *Outlines of the Geographical Distribution of British Plants* (1832) contained the embryonic idea for this method which later developed into the vice-county system which is used today.

The first book by Turner and Dillwyn owed a great deal to the records supplied by the two eminent Welsh botanists J.W. Griffith and the Reverend Hugh Davies. The later work of Watson however, as far as Snowdonia was concerned, relied on records published in the 1805 version and information only available to him in manuscript, as Watson explains in his note preceeding the Caernarfonshire catalogue on pages 235-244 of his book.

'On this account, I regret not having the means of giving a complete list of the rarer plants within it. Such are very little known to me from actual observation, notwithstanding that the county has been thrice visited, but unluckily at very unfit periods for mountain botany . . . Indeed I have usually found it more difficult to get the stations for plants only moderately scarce or of partial occurance, than for those of decided rarity.'

Watson relied on the records of Nathaniel J. Winch (1768-1838) copied from the *Magazine of Natural History*, of which the plants were all gathered by himself; the *Botanist's Guide* of 1805; and the manuscripts of J.E. Bowman and C.C. Babington.

John Eddowes Bowman (1785-1841) was born on 30 October 1785 at Nantwich, Cheshire, and following his education at the grammar school he left to work in his father's tobacconist's business becoming manager of the manufacturing department, and traveller. He lost his wealth in 1816 after the failure of a banking business which he had joined as a junior partner in 1813. His fortunes soon took a turn for the better, however, and he became manager of the Welshpool branch of the bank of Beck and Co., of Shrewsbury. In 1824 he moved to Wrexham to manage another bank and retired from business in 1830. He lived in Manchester from 1837 onwards, interesting himself in several different branches of science and was one of the founders of the Manchester Geological Society, and he was a fellow of both the Linnean and Geological Societies. His more important discoveries were in relation to the lower plants, chiefly mosses and fungi. Like William Wilson of Warrington, he was a frequent visitor to North Wales staying at the Bangor home of John Roberts (mentioned earlier), who accompanied him on many of his botanical rambles.

William Wilson (1799-1871) was a native of Warrington and the second son of Thomas Wilson, a local chemist. He attended the Prestbury Grammar School and completed his education at the Dissenters' Academy in Leaf Square, Manchester. He entered the legal profession being articled as a pupil to Messers Barratt and Wilson, solicitors at Manchester. Over-committment to his studies led to a deterioration in his health, and in a bid to combat his illness he found it necessary to take holidays and undertake long journeys. William Wilson had a keen interest in natural history from an early age and while on these lonely rambles he began to study botany. During the years 1824 and 1825 his mother offered him a sum of money, the interest of which would enable him to pursue his adopted studies and resign his position with the Manchester firm of solicitors. At first he hesitated to give up the law, but his precarious state of health eventually persuaded him.

In 1826 Sir James Edward Smith (1759-1828) was so impressed with a parcel of plants, together with notes on the various species, that Wilson had sent him that he immediately invited him to become one of his correspondents. Smith, the country's leading botanist at the time, replied to Wilson in a letter dated 10 May of that year; this letter convinced Wilson not only to adopt botany as a relaxation, but also as his life's work. 'More letters to answer,' wrote Smith as he penned the thoughts which entered his mind upon receiving Wilson's parcel, 'The more I write the more I receive! I had not for some moments courage to open it. But when I did, how was my tone changed! Instead of idle questions, I found such an assemblage of varieties and novelties as have rarely met my eyes, accompanied with so much excellent intelligence and such kind offers as made me put everything else aside and resign myself to that pure pleasure which botany . . . has so often afforded me. Be pleased, therefore, Sir, to accept in the first place my grateful thanks for your liberality and kindness to an entire stranger, but (I hope) to one who will not prove unworthy . . . Any important corrections or remarks cannot but be welcome from your pen'. So wrote the foremost botanical authority in the land; words that were to encourage the modest young Wilson to pursue his favourite science to the utmost of his capabilities.

Two more distinguished botanists joined the ranks of Wilson's ever increasing band of correspondents. Sir William Jackson Hooker (1785-1865) then professor of botany at Glasgow, asked for Wilson's expertise in preperation for a forthcoming issue of the *Flora Londinensis*, and on 17 April 1827 introductions were made through Professor John Stevens Henslow (1796-1861) of Cambridge, who had been acquainted with the young botanist since May 1826. A letter from Hooker to Wilson dated 16 May 1827 recommends the study of mosses as a field in need of attention; Hooker also acknowledges Wilson's valuable help and invites him to join his class on a five day botanical excursion among the Breadalbane Hills which was accepted. Wilson prolonged his stay in the vicinity of Killin until mid September.

Hooker wrote to Wilson's mother following the botanical excursion, assuring her of her son's improving health, adding that he had sailed from Glasgow to the Isle of Man; the letter continues: 'He was so agreeable an inmate of our house that I assure you both myself and all my family are looking forward to his paying us some future visit with very great pleasure. There are few persons in whom I have felt so much interest upon so short an acquaintance'. Thus began the friendship and collaboration between Hooker and Wilson which lasted all their lives.

Wilson then spent two years in Ireland, making some of his most important discoveries. In 1830 Charles Edward Sowerby (1795-1842) and his brother James De Carle Sowerby (1787-1871) were engaged in the publication of the *Supplement to English Botany* (1831-40); Wilson illustrated and described various plants newly discovered in Britain, for that work. He gathered specimens of the rare fern oblong woodsia (*Woodsia ilvensis*) from the Devil's Kitchen above Cwm Idwal, furnishing fronds for the illustrator to copy, and also the Wilson's filmy-fern (*Hymenophyllum wilsonii*) to which he appends the following note after the usual descriptive comments. It should be remembered that prior to this period the British filmy-fern (*Hymenophyllum*) was considered to be only one species, *H.tunbrigense*. 'So very different in aspect is this truly distinct species from the far more elegant *H.tunbridgense* that no one who has had the good fortune to see them luxuriantly growing in company in the rocky woods that border the wild and sequestered upper lake of Killarney would hesitate to pronounce them two species. It was there that in the summer of 1829 I became first acquainted with the true *Hymenophyllum tunbridgense*, and had at once the gratification of clearing up my doubts concerning the spurious kind, with which as the common *Hymenophyllum* of North Wales, Cumberland and Perthshire, I had long been imperfectly familiar, and also of unexpectedly adding another fern to the British Flora'.

William Wilson published nothing under his own name until his *magnum opus* appeared in 1855. *Bryologia Britannica* contained descriptions of all the known mosses of Britain and Ireland systematically arranged according to the method of Brüch and Schimper; it was a much enlarged third edition of Hooker and Taylor's standard work called *Muscologia Britannica*, including many additions and alterations. Editions with coloured illustrations were offered at 4 guineas per copy and those with black and white illustrations at 2 guineas.

Earlier in his career Wilson had assisted Hooker as he prepared his *English Flora* (1830) and this help is acknowledged frequently with remarks such as, 'I am glad to have Mr Wilson's authority for this,' and 'I am supported in this view by Mr Wilson,' etc.

J.E. Bowman introduced himself to William Wilson by letter in May 1830 stating that he had of late added the study of mosses to his long-standing interest in vascular plants. (Flowering plants and ferns.) A letter dated 26 March 1831 reads thus: 'I first began to dabble in botany in 1807. For the first 10 years I knew only a few common plants, and I did not preserve a single specimen; and for twenty years it was not my fortune to come into personal contact with any one who could be called a botanist, or to whom I could apply for a solution to my difficulties or the correction of my errors'. In his first letter Bowman mentions his intention of spending a week botanizing among the Snowdonian hills adding that nothing would give him more pleasure than to have Wilson accompanying him. Wilson reciprocated such feelings and with his reply sent specimens of a rare moss he had gathered in Ireland. Bowman's reply is lengthy and in anticipation of Wilson being able to accompany him in Snowdonia writes: 'I am happy to find that there is some prospect of your being able to accompany me on my projected Snowdonian ramble. From your extensive knowledge of Snowdonia I will leave you to fix the plan for that ramble'. There follows a long discussion on plant taxonomy, (or naming system) habitats and various potential areas for plant hunting; Bowman, despite being the elder of the two men was at all times modest; cautious not to overstate his experiences or capabilities and he always regarded Wilson as being the master. 'Nor have I been entirely unsuccessful in the way of discovery during my short career' he writes 'though I cannot boast, with you, of having added a new phanerogamous plant to our native flora, and, that to the confusion of Welsh botanists, upon our own hills too'. Bowman evidently considered himself a 'Welsh botanist'.

Both Wilson and Bowman were regular visitors to North Wales either independently, together or as the guests of Dr John Roberts at Bangor. In a letter to Hooker sent from Bangor in May 1828, Wilson regrets having only made 'short excursions in the neighbourhood' due to the 'general badness of the weather' and proceeds to write a lengthy note on botanical matters, noting that sadly he had 'not yet penetrated far into the mountainous regions'.

He was at Bangor again in July of that year, this time in the company of Nathaniel J. Winch whom he had guided to the stations of some of the neighbourhood's more interesting plants. Wilson wrote to Hooker on the 23rd. 'Long before your highly welcome letter reached me Mr Winch had taken his departure, & I was unable, during the very short stay that he made to do more than conduct him to some of the stations of the rarer plants which I had already gathered, and we had not time to explore the mountains in making any new discoveries nor did we even visit Snowdon so that what we did amounts to very little . . . ' There follows a very interesting passage concerning his recent botanical observations. '*Jungermannia Hutchinsiae* (barren) is plentiful in one station near Llanberis, & lately found *J.Lyellii* with anthers, pistilla, & calyces in Anglesea near Aberffraw not far from the sea side on a wet sandy common growing in clustered patches, male & female seperate . . . *J.compressa* with anthers, & sparingly with capsules, upon Snowdon . . . *Gymnostomum Griffithianum [Oedipodium griffithianum]* is in notable plenty upon Snowdon near the summit . . . I observed *Hookeria lucens* very near the summit of one of the peaks of Snowdon at an elevation of not less than 3000 feet. *Anthericum serotinum* [Snowdon lily; *(Lloydia serotina)*] has not flowered well this summer, & the wet weather hindered me from gathering above two or three specimens in a fit state . . . ' Wilson then proceeds to discuss the many-stalked spike-rush *(Eleocharis multicaulis)* and supports Hugh Davies' description of the plant in *Welsh Botanology*. 'Of *Eleocharis multicaulis* I have secured some good characteristic specimens which will I trust, leave the question no longer doubtful. It is most surprising to me that Wahlenberg should deny the presence of a creeping root in *E.pa.* [*E.palustris*] I shall send you specimens of both . . . Old Hugh Davies has well distinguished them in *Welsh Botanology E.multicaulis* having constantly six bristles at the base of the germen *&* *E.palustris* as constantly 4 only . . . ' Wilson however disagreed with Davies concerning the recording of the field pepperwort *Lepidium campestre* in *Welsh Botanology*. 'It is very little to the credit of Davies or myself as diligent botanists, that *Lepidium hirtum* should have been so long overlooked in Anglesea — it was only early in June last that I observed it for the first time. I believe it is the only *Lepidium* growing wild in Anglesea having never been able to find *L.campestre,* for which Davies has probably mistaken *L.hirtum* . . . *L.campestre* is very rare also in Caernarvonshire while *hirtum* is quite abundant in both counties'. In his *Flora of Anglesey and Carnarvonshire* (1894/5) J.E. Griffith has this to say on the matter: 'Mr William Wilson (in his MSS notes on Davies' *Welsh Botanology* which I now possess) remarks about this plant as follows: "Must be very rare in Anglesey and probably mistaken by Davies for *Lepidium Smithii* which is very common all over Anglesey". I quite agree with Mr Wilson as I have never seen *L.campestre* growing in either of the two counties'. Modern-day botanists know the plant in question as smith's pepperwort or smith's cress *(Lepidum heterophyllum)* and it has been recorded from both Anglesey and Caernarfonshire.

By 1830 Wilson's connections with North Wales had become personal as well as botanical. In a letter to Hooker written at Aberffraw in Anglesey on 15 September 1830 he begins with an apology for not having replied to a letter due to a 'very unwelcome occupation which still detains me here & almost bans me from botanical pursuits. A sister in law whose a widow with a small precarious income has removed from Staffordshire to this neighbourhood in expectation of finding a cheap [-] residence with the advantages of sea air and bathing — the goods were prematurely brought over before the house had undergone the necessary alterations & everything has been in confusion'. On 13 August, J.E.

Bowman arrived and spent a week with Wilson, who owing to his predicament, was unable to give him much of his time. During his stay Bowman made an important discovery, a new British species of waterwort (*Elatine*). Although not named by Wilson in his letter, this was most probably the eight-stamened waterwort (*Elatine hydropiper*) found at Llyn Coron, north east of Aberffraw. This was included by W.J. Hooker in his *British Flora*, published in 1831.

The same letter mentions 'the Snowdon sketches' which were presumably drawn by Wilson and despatched to Hooker. 'Pray consider yourself at liberty to make any use you think of the Snowdon sketches, there is one consideration however which I would wish you to make & that is whether an unfair use will not be made of them by indolent botanists or rapacious mercenary gardeners . . . I have known tourists to send up their guides for plants, while they remain below, and what they had [-] paid for, they would probably boast of as their own genuine acquisitions'. The 'Illustrations of Snowdon — Botanical and Geographical', are preserved at the Royal Botanic Gardens, Kew, (Archives) among the correspondence of Sir W.J. Hooker. These sketches drawn from Treborth near the Telford bridge and the cromlech at Plas Newydd Anglesey, show an outline of the Snowdonian range of mountains with the names of the various peaks, ridges, lakes and 'cwms' and some of the rare plants found there, annotated above.

The notebook of William Wilson is kept at the Natural History Museum together with his Herbarium. A note on the cover of the notebook written when it was acquired in 1903 reads 'This book is of value as affording a legible transcript of names of localities which are not clearly written on labels in the Herbm'. The mountain plants listed include:

Interrupted clubmoss (*Lycopodium annotinum*) from Glyder
Dwarf juniper (*Juniperis communis ssp. alpina*) from Glyder
Black alpine-sedge (*Carex atrata*) from Twll Du
Holly fern (*Polystichum lonchitis*) from Cwm Idwal
Forked spleenwort (*Asplenium septentrionale*) near Twll Du
Oblong woodsia (*Woodsia ilvensis*) near Llyn y Cŵn
Wilson's filmy-fern (*Hymenophyllum wilsonii*) near Llanberis

alpine saxifrage (*Saxifraga nivalis*) mossy saxifrage (*Saxifraga hypnoides*) and *Cerastium latifolium* from Snowdon. The latter named plant could be either *C.alpinum* of *C.arcticum* as Wilson does not specify the exact spot from which the plant was gathered. Both these species have in the past been recorded from Snowdon. J.E. Griffith in his *Flora of Anglesey and Carnarvonshire* (1894/5) page 23 notes the following regarding the arctic mouse-ear (*Cerastium arcticum*): 'I always took this to be *C.latifolium*, Sm., till Rev. A. Ley, had it determined, through Mr A. Bennett, by Dr Lange. See J.[ournal] of B.[otany] p.373, 1887'.

Lesser meadow-rue *(Thalictrum minus)* Snowdon

Spring sandwort *(Minuartia verna)* Cwm Idwal

Alpine penny-cress *(Thlaspi caerulescens)* Gwydir. This plant was most probably shown to Wilson by John Roberts of Bangor whose name is appended to the entry.

The plants of Anglesey and Caernarfonshire are listed in the notebook on five pages being numbered from one to eighty-four.

In 1836 William Wilson married Mrs Lane, a cousin of his, at St Pancras Church, London, and from then on his botanical excursions became curtailed as the modest private income, which had served him so adequately during his bachelor days, was now needed to support a family. He died on 3 April 1871 at Paddington, about two miles from Warrington.

Babington's Journal

Another eminent botanist who found himself drawn to Snowdonia and visited the district regularly throughout his long life was Charles Cardale Babington (1808-1895). He was born in Ludlow, Shropshire on 23 November 1808, the son of the Reverend Joseph Babington (1768-1826), physician and Rector who also studied plants contributing to J. Plumley's *General View of Agriculture of Shropshire* (1803, 180-211), and Sowerby and Smith's *English Botany*. Charles Babington took his B.A. degree at Cambridge in January 1830 and in July of the same year embarked on his first 'Welsh Tour'. He travelled by coach entering Wales from Shrewsbury and continued along the Holyhead road through Betws-y-coed to Bangor, accompanied by three friends, Mallet, Hockin and Fleming. The next day, 7 July, the party walked a distance of 10½

Charles Cardale Babington (1808-1895)

miles from their lodgings to Caernarfon, arriving at the Uxbridge Arms wet through, having walked the last 7 miles in continuous rain.

Having secured lodgings at Caernarfon, they spent a few days botanizing in the neighbourhood of the town and on the 11th, being a Sunday, they attended service at St Mary's Church which Babington says 'is a neat one, having one of its sides formed of part of the town wall, and its tower being a round stunted one belonging originally to the same'. On the 12th he records opium poppy (*Papaver somniferum*), rosebay willowherb (*Chamerion angustifolium*) and sweet violet (*Viola odorata*) 'with blue flowers, in a corn field near the town, but on the other side of the river, where there are no houses, or I would have thought them cultivated'. The following day he and his colleagues travelled to the vale of Llanberis with the intention of finding their way to the mountains. There is no mention of a guide being sought for; the weather being favourable they attempted to find their own way but soon ran into difficulties 'by taking what we supposed would be a short cut, arrived at the river having only a foot bridge over it, with a gate in the middle well guarded with spikes. The bridge was formed of two planks parallel to each other, and bent into an elliptical arch by being fastened tight to the rock on each side without any support in the middle. Being stopped by this, we had to return nearly three quarters of a mile, and then continued the road we were in before. After having crossed the river by a stone bridge further up, we were foolish enough to take another short cut which appeared to lead to the mountains, which we followed for about two miles, and then stopped to examine a bog in which we found nothing worth having, and then turned back, not having time to go further'. Only two plants are recorded for the day, annual knawel (*Scleranthus annuus*) and lady's-mantle (*Alchemilla vulgaris*).

During the days which followed the weather took a turn for the worse, the wind rose and they only ventured outside to collect a few plants and insects from localities close by. There are no entries in the journal from the 19th to the 31st of July. On the 31st with his friend Mallet, Babington again journeyed to Llanberis by taking a boat from Pen llyn at the lower end of Llyn Padarn and disembarking at a point close to Pont y bala. They then walked up to Nant Peris village, which Babington refers to as Llanberis in his journal, 'the road to which is only passable for horses; it passes under the enormous precipices of Snowdon, near a copper mine'. They stayed the night at the Dolbadarn Inn, with a view to ascending Snowdon on the following day, but the weather changed for the worse forcing them to change their plans.

Babington and his colleague ascended Moel Eilio on 13 August, the view from the summit being considered adequate recompense for the uninteresting climbing; the 15th saw the two on the summit opposite. Babington found his first mountain saxifrage while climbing Mynydd Mawr, this plant being the starry saxifrage (*Saxifraga stellaris*). Also recorded were parsley fern

(*Cryptogramma crispa*) and autumnal starwort (*Callitriche hermaphroditica*) the latter seen 'in great plenty in the river which runs out of Llyn Cwellyn'. He returned to Mynydd Mawr on the 29th to look for insects 'but found no land ones, and only some water ones; got quite wet through by a storm on the top of the mountain'.

On 31 August Babington ascended Snowdon for the first time, taking no guide. The entry in the journal records no difficulties. 'Obtained a large number of plants in the rocks near the mouth of the copper mine', he states, but fails to give any indication as to the location he visited, which could be either the Clogwyn Coch mine near Clogwyn Du'r Arddu or the Snowdon mine near Llyn Glaslyn. Both these sites were much frequented by botanists during their visits to Snowdon. Babington claimed to have taken a thirty-two mile walk on 1 September. On the preceding day he had walked up Snowdon and returned to the Dolbadarn Inn where he spent the night. 'Started at a quarter past eight in the morning, and after ascending part of Glydr-y-Vawr, passed through Llanberis Pass, at the head of which I ascended another mountain on the left, [probably Moel Berfedd] Descended into Nant Gwynant, which I followed to Beddgelert, where I dined, and afterwards walked back to Carnarvon. Whilst my dinner was cooking, I walked to Pont Aberglasllyn, which is about a mile and a half from Beddgelert. Total distance in day about thirty-two miles'. On 4 September Babington, in the company of Mallet, again walked up Snowdon reaching the summit at 2.00 p.m. In this entry he again refers to 'the face of the precipice in which the copper mine is', as the site from where he gathered plant specimens, and from where 'we ascended to the top, and re-visited both the tops . . . ' This suggests that Clogwyn y Garnedd was the precipice in question, but none of the plants found there are noted in the journal. The pair then descended the mountain by following the track known today as the Rhyd Ddu path, but lost all trace of it lower down. After a great deal of trouble the Beddgelert road was reached at a point about three miles outside the village.

Babington's first visit to Snowdonia ended on 11 September; he left Caernarfon on the 10th but did not arrive in Bangor in time for the Shrewsbury coach. He left at 7.00 a.m. on the following morning.

He returned in 1832, leaving Shrewsbury at a quarter to six on the morning of 27 June and notes in his journal the fine view of the Snowdonian range of mountains from the vicinity of the inn at Cernioge near Pentrefoelas. On the 28th he walked from Bangor to view the slate quarries at Dolawen, the property of Mr Pennant, Penrhyn Castle. 'They are now cut into the very heart of the mountain,' he writes 'and employ more than 1600 men. The slates are conveyed by a railroad to Port Penrhyn near Bangor, from which place they are shipped, twelve shiploads having this year gone from them to America'. On the 29th he went to Caernarfon by coach at 9.00 a.m. and began to walk up to

Llanberis with a view to seeking accommodation for a few days. This he obtained at the Vaynol Arms in Nant Peris where the landlord being Robert Closs charged a shilling for a bed and a shilling for a meal. On the following day Babington, in the company of two other botanists he names as Holmes and Leighton, walked part of the way up Snowdon, finding mossy saxifrage (*Saxifraga hypnoides*) roseroot (*Sedum rosea*) parsley fern (*Cryptogramma crispa*) and marsh violet (*Viola palustris*). His two colleagues during this trip were most probably the Reverend Edward Adolphus Holmes (?-1886) and the Reverend William Allport Leighton (1805-1889). On the same day after dinner they 'walked a short distance up the Llanberis Pass, or Cwmglas, as it is called in Welsh'. Leighton was the author of the *Lichen Flora of Great Britain, Ireland and the Channel Islands* published in 1871, with another edition in 1879. His personal records number around 287, observed not only from the old classic botanical sites such as Snowdon, Cwm Idwal and the Glyder mountains, but from places further afield in the county such as Nefyn, Pwllheli, Cricieth, Conwy, Gwydir Woods and Moel y Gest near Porthmadog. Holmes, the other botanist named was Rector at South Elsham, Suffolk from 1833 until his death on 3 June 1886.

On 2 July Babington again visited Snowdon, this time ascending the ridge of hills which rise steeply behind Nant Peris Church. The precise line of path is not stated. Having gained the crest of the ridge he turned left and followed the Pony track towards the summit. Ascending the steep bank called Llechwedd y Re he soon arrived at the spring near Bwlch Glas where 'the horses of those who ride up are left'. In his entry for the day Babington names Clogwyn y Garnedd as the precipice from which he gathered such rare plants as alpine saxifrage (*Saxifraga nivalis*) tufted saxifrage (*Saxifraga cespitosa*) arctic mouse-ear (*Cerastium arcticum*) and spring sandwort (*Minuartia verna*). On the 5th he went to Clogwyn Du'r Arddu, finding there brittle bladder-fern (*Cystopteris fragilis*) green spleenwort (*Asplenium trichomanes-ramosum*) alpine meadow-rue (*Thalictrum alpinum*) tufted saxifrage (*Saxifraga cespitosa*) globeflower (*Trollius europaeus*) and northern rock-cress (*Arabis petraea*).

Babington's excursion to the Glyder from Nant Peris on 10 July is worth noting as it describes a route to Llyn y Cŵn which was probably in use from the earliest times. 'We went by direction up the stream opposite the inn until we came to the place where two streams and an empty channel meet, then turned to the right up the mountain, and on our arrival at the top kept rather to the left between the one which we ascended and the next (i.e. due east), and soon arrived at Llyn y Cwm'. [Cŵn]. He then followed the stream from the lake to the top of the Devil's Kitchen chasm. 'We tried hard to find a place at which it would be possible to descend to the bottom of the fissure where it opens in the face of the precipice called Castell y Geifr over Llyn Idwal. After some time we found on the south side a way down a ledge of rocks (near the top of which I found *Gnaphalium dioicum* [mountain everlasting (*Antennaria dioica*)] which led us to the lower opening of the fissure. We then went along a narrow ledge on the other side of the stream, which, after leading us for some way along the face of the precipice and under a sort of showerbath, took us with some exertion to the top of the rocks'. Having arrived back on the plateau close to Llyn y Cŵn, Babington then decided to climb Glyder Fawr and having arrived at an 'eminence' he calls in his journal 'Carnedd y Gwynt' he found the wind so strong that he could hardly stand against it. He then returned to Nant Peris by the same route as that by which he had ascended.

On 12 July after a period of heavy rain, Babington found the waterfall of Ceunant Mawr Llanberis in spate; he then spent the remainder of the day botanizing at the lower end of Llyn Padarn where he found pillwort (*Pilularia globulifera*), water lobelia (*Lobelia dortmanna*) and white water-lily (*Nymphaea alba*). On the following day he took the Capel Curig coach to Swallow Falls and found near it Wilson's filmy-fern (*Hymenophyllum wilsonii*) and oak fern (*Gymnocarpium dryopteris*). About a mile from Pen y gwryd on the Capel Curig side, he notes having found ivy-leaved bellflower (*Wahlenbergia hederacea*) in plenty. On the following day he was on Snowdon again and counted twenty-nine lakes to be seen from the summit. Descending to Clogwyn y Garnedd to botanize, he noted the much sought after holly fern (*Polystichum lonchitis*) in his journal for the first time.

Another important discovery is noted in the journal for 16 July when Babington visited the Llyn y Cŵn area and continued on to the summit of Glyder Fawr. On the way back his friend Holmes found small quantities of the interrupted clubmoss (*Lycopodium annotinum*). This rare clubmoss was first found in the same area by Edward Lhuyd during one of his visits to Snowdonia in the 17th century. William Wilson of Warrington recorded having seen it in 1836; this being the last time the plant was seen to grow on the Glyder above Llyn y Cŵn. J.E. Griffith's *Flora of Anglesey and Carnarvonshire* (1894/5) has this to say on the matter on page 171. 'I am afraid this is extinct in Carnarvonshire. It used to grow on the Glyders, but I have failed to find it for years now'.

A search in the Llanberis area resulted in their finding Wilson's filmy fern on the 17th and the following day Babington in the company of Holmes walked over the Llanberis Pass as far as Pen y gwryd; on returning there finding the forked spleenwort (*Asplenium septentrionale*) in small quantities on rocks at the lower end of the pass. On the 19th Babington again climbed Snowdon by an obscure route which led from behind the church at Nant Peris and on gaining the ridge descended a short distance joining the Pony track from Llanberis and followed it to Llechwedd y Re from where he descended into Cwmglas Mawr. 'We then ascended a precipice near to Crib Coch and found, after we had gone some way, that we could not return, so were obliged to go to the top of it'. The two plants noted in the journal from the day's excursion were alpine bistort (*Persicaria vivipara*) and hoary whitlow-grass (*Draba incana*); both plants being rare, but still extant in this area. 'The place to which we came on the top of the precipice was a grassy ridge between Crib Coch and Crib-y-Distill. For some time we could not find a way from it, but at last, after some hard climbing, we attained the summit of the mountain and returned home'. The plant-collectors' vascula (collecting flasks) must have contained considerably more specimens that day than the two above named plants, judging from the entry in the journal for the 20th. 'Did not start soon on account of the number of plants wanting to be looked over'. Having completed this task the botanists spent the remaining hours of the 20th gathering wetland plants from area surrounding the shores of Llyn Padarn. The collecting continued on the 21st. 'Started early and went up Snowdon to examine another part of Clogwyn y Garnedd . . . We then set to work at Clogwyn y Garnedd, and I found one specimen of *Carex atrata* [black alpine sedge] and Holmes one of *Epilobium alsinifolium*. [chickweed willowherb] 'We found about thirty specimens of *Saxifraga nivalis* [alpine saxifrage] in Clogwyn y Garnedd . . . '

The remaining days of Babington's second (1832) tour of North Wales were spent in the Dolgellau district and in exploring Cadair Idris. 'Cader Idris. July 23. Started to walk to Dolgelly to see Cader Idris. Went by the Capel Curig coach as far as the top of the pass, and met with Mr D. Williams, agent to Sir R. Bulkeley . . . He put us into a track over the mountains to Festiniog, but the track not being at all well marked we nearly lost our way, and had it not been for the map and my compass seal, we must have turned back, but with the assistance of these we at length found our way to that part of the vale near Llyn Cwmorthin. The road, or rather way, for path there is none, was very wild and dreary, but the prospects from some parts very fine and extensive. Not knowing in what part of the vale Festiniog was situated we passed it, and walked two-and-a-half miles to Maentwrog. This was a very hard days work.'

The remainder of the journey was completed on the 24th by following the road from Maentwrog to Trawsfynydd and on through Llanelltyd to Dolgellau. The following morning Babington employed the services of W.R. Pugh, the well-known guide, and climbed Cadair Idris. They crossed Mynydd Moel and Bwlch Coch before descending to the road and made their way to Dinas Mawddwy, arriving there in the evening. The only plant recorded during the ascent of Cadair Idris was 'a very hairy corolla'd *Festuca*' [fescue]. They left Dinas Mawddwy on the 26th and followed the course of the river Dyfi to Llanymawddwy, crossed the 'very lofty pass of Bwlch-y-Groes from the top of which the prospect was most extensive'. They later arrived at Bala and stayed overnight at the Lion, 'a most excellent inn'. From Bala they walked to Ffestiniog along the 'old road' a distance of over nineteen miles; continuing from there to Maentwrog where they stopped for the night. On the

28th they were on the road to Beddgelert before 6.30 a.m. and breakfasted there on arrival. Soon afterwards they struck the road again walking through Nantgwynant to Pen y gwryd and over into Llanberis, a total distance of twenty-two miles according to Babington. The 1832 tour came to an end on 3 August when the journal records 'Started for Shrewsbury'. By the end of his second botanical tour of Snowdonia, Babington had a good knowledge of the plant localities of Snowdon and Glyder as well as the Isle of Anglesey. There is no mention in the journal of a local guide being taken on any of these early excursions apart from Pugh who led him to Cadair Idris. It must therefore be assumed that Babington, in the company of a few friends, explored the cliffs and 'cwms' of Eryri without any local help.

At a later date in his journal, and also among other correspondence however, there is evidence to suggest that Babington had at different times acquired the services of three local men to act as guides on various mountain excursions. They were John Roberts, William Williams and Hugh Lewis, who according to the 1861 census returns lived in houses known collectively as Blaen y ddôl in Llanberis. The two first named served as guides for the Royal Victoria Hotel, while Hugh Lewis (in whose house William Williams was a lodger) seems only to have acted as guide on a casual basis.

In August 1862 the distinguished French botanist J. Gay visited Snowdonia, primarily to study the quillwort (*Isoetes*) and Babington recorded in his journal his meeting with Gay at Bangor on the 12th. On the following day Babington, together with Gay and the Reverend William Williamson Newbould went to stay at the Padarn Villa Hotel at Llanberis. They walked around the shores of Llyn Padarn finding quillwort (*Isoetes echinospora*) 'near Ynys, on the left bank'. More specimens of quillwort was found in Llyn y Cŵn on the 15th; Babington records 'Mr Gay was very much fatigued by his trip to Llyn y Cwm'. [Cŵn] There are references to John Roberts the guide in Gay's published account of his visit entitled: *Voyage botanique au Caernarvonshire, dans le North Wales fait en Aout 1862 en vue d'une étude particuliere des Isoetes de cette contrée* . . . (see J. Gay, Bull. de le Sov. Bot. de France x, 1863).

Another reference to John Roberts the guide appears in the entry in Babington's journal dated 24 September 1860. 'Busk, his brother Charles, and I went with John Roberts, the guide, to Cwm Glas, by ascending highly on Snowdon, and descending into it. We went as far as the saddle of turf by Crib Goch, and descended into Llanberis Pass'. The same John Roberts was also involved in the running of one of the Snowdon summit huts which provided tourists with refreshments.

William Williams, the 'botanical guide' or 'Will Boots' as he was known locally, is not mentioned anywhere in Babington's journal, but there is no doubt that Babington knew Williams and this acquaintance will be dealt with in a later chapter.

On 4 September 1865 Babington notes the following regarding Hugh Lewis: 'With Hugh Lewis to a spot high up on the further side of the mass of mountain which projects into the pass on the left side to see *Asplenium alternifolium* [the hybrid alternate-leaved spleenwort]. He shewed me one small plant of it, and knows of another. Saw plenty of *A.septentrionale*'. [forked spleenwort] It would appear therefore that most of the local guides of Snowdonia were well acquainted with the localities of the rare plants.

In 1835 Babington became acquainted with John Roberts the surgeon and botanist from Bangor, mentioned in a previous chapter, and on 29 July of that year the journal records that both men visited the classical botanical site of Clogwyn Du'r Arddu.

On the 30th, Babington went to Clogwyn y Garnedd but failed in his quest to find the tiny rare fern alpine woodsia (*Woodsia alpina*). An interesting entry in the journal dated 11 August 1847 reads: 'By coach to Capel Curig. Met Wollaston at Cerrig y drudion on his return from Wales. Examined the rounded hill opposite to the turn to Capel Curig from the main road to see if we could find *Cotoneaster*, said by Kingsley of Sidney to grow there, but we could find nothing like it, except a *Salix*. Do not believe that it grows there, as it is not a likely place for it'. On the morning of the 13th, Babington took a carriage from Capel Curig to Nant Peris with the intention of booking in at the Vaynol Arms, but on arriving there he found that the former landlord and his family had gone to America. Moving on, he found what he describes as 'excellent quarters' at the Dolbadarn Inn, which served ideally as a base from which to explore Snowdon. He explored the whole length of the base of Clogwyn Du'r Arddu finding the Snowdon lily (*Lloydia serotina*); Babington was fortunate to see the plant so late in the season. Normally the Snowdon lily flowers for only a few short weeks between late May and June, after which time only the long slender rush-like leaves remain. He was lucky again on the 18th after climbing from Nant Peris to Llyn y Cŵn, 'in a thick cloud on the mountain; we saw Twll Dhû to great advantage both from above and below. I gathered one fruited plant of Lloydia a little before reaching the lower opening of Twll Dhû.'

The journal is full of similar comments. Babington remained a regular visitor to Snowdonia all his life, becoming Professor of Botany at Cambridge in 1861, and he missed no opportunity to see, in their natural habitats, the plants about which he taught.

The Great Victorian Fern Craze

As the 19th century progressed geographical plant distribution developed into a major study among British botanists. Hewett Cottrell Watson (1804-1881), noted previously, pioneered a system which was based on dividing Britain into areas he called 'vice-counties' starting with West Cornwall, vice-county number 1, and ending with the Shetland Isles, vice-county number 112. This enabled the plant distribution system to be conveniently displayed using maps. Of the thirteen Welsh vice-counties Caernarfonshire provided the longest and most interesting list of plants published by Watson in his *New Botanist's Guide to the Localities of the Rarer Plants of Britain*.

Watson's greatest work *Topographical Botany* was first published in 1873-74, with a second edition appearing in 1883, two years after his death. The vice-county system had by this time been perfected and was used for the first time in this work.

Records of Snowdonian plants were frequently published during the 19th century, appearing in the printed works of visiting naturalists, local guide books, and in various issues of botanical journals. These botanical records were usually supported by voucher specimens which were gathered from the habitats in unlimited quantities. An ever increasing number of members of the upper and middle classes adopted this pastime during the 1830s, the forming of a personal and complete *hortus siccus* being their ultimate target of achievement. Another major trend to coincide with this was the great Victorian

Holly fern (Polystichum lonchitis) photo: Griff Williams

129

fern craze. Up until this time few field botanists had taken any special interest in ferns; the field offered but a limited challenge to the collectors due to the relatively small number of British species. In order to constitute a wider field of interest the fern enthusiasts began to look for varieties among each separate species and these were either dried and pressed in their albums or transplanted into their gardens at home.

The classical regions of Snowdonia, while continuing to attract visiting botanists now began to experience a new kind of collector in the plant hunters. The local people soon began to realize that they could profit from the demand for plant specimens, especially from the ferns; unlimited supplies of the more common species were always available by the wayside. These were gathered by the basketful and sold to visitors as rarities. For supplying genuine specimens of rarities to the specialist collector, a different kind of supplier was needed. 'Alpines' such as holly fern (*Polystichum lonchitis*) for instance, could be acquired through the services of the mountain guides and the copper miners. These men were accustomed to finding their way across the mountains in any weather, and were, due to their station in life, always eager for an opportunity to supplement their family income.

In his autobiography, Welsh botanist John Lloyd Williams (1854-1945) gives a vivid account of his experiences, and of some of the collectors he encountered during the great collecting era. The fern collecting mania lasted throughout the Victorian age, reaching its peak during the 1860s, but the gathering of plant specimens in general continued throughout the 19th century, and as many will testify, well into the 20th.

John Lloyd Williams was born in 1854 at Plas Isa, Llanrwst according to his autobiography. Plas Isa was once the home of the celebrated William Salesbury mentioned in Chapter 1, of who Lloyd Williams refers to when he says 'these walls did not transfer to me a particle of the scholar's gift': modest words from a man who, among his varied achievements, had been a Professor of Botany. He was educated at the British School, Llanrwst and later entered the Normal College, Bangor as the holder of a Queen's Scholarship where he studied for a teaching career. He was appointed headmaster of the Garn Dolbenmaen school in 1875, and during his spare time there he pursued his botanical interests and continued to develop his musical talents. He became a prominent figure at concerts and in eisteddfodic circles as a conductor and adjudicator. He subsequently studied botany at the Royal College of Science, London under Sir John Bretland Farmer (1865-1944) and returned to Bangor to commence his botanical researches as a member of the staff of the University College of North Wales obtaining in 1906 a D.Sc of the University of Wales. He was appointed to the Chair of Botany at Aberystwyth in 1914, where he continued with the studies of seaweeds which he had began at Bangor. These marine studies were to become his classic thesis, but botany was not the only field of

J. Lloyd Williams (1854-1945)
(courtesy of the National Museum of Wales)

study in which he achieved distinction. He became an Honorary Doctor of
Music of the University of Wales in 1936, and with Dr Mary Davies laid the
foundations for the Welsh Folk Song Society.

J. Lloyd Williams' interest in natural history began during boyhood years.
In his autobiography *Atgofion Tri-Chwarter Canrif*, published in four volumes
between 1941 and 1945, he recalls how he used to be more inclined to study the
behaviour of birds rather than just collect eggs. He also began to collect insects,
noting the different species and studying their habits with the aid of a crudely
fashioned pocket lens of his own design. This he made using a piece of glass
onto which a drop of glue was dropped and it served as a lens as long as the glue
remained in a convex form. Another device which was used to study small
creatures was simply a glass tumbler filled with water. The insects were placed
inside the receptacle and examined as they swam close to the swollen patterns
of the glass. He collected all manner of natural curiosities; these were stored in
boxes with glass lids. His bedroom served as a laboratory and also as a room
where he housed his 'museum', as he calls it. There were also collections of
mosses and ferns, dried, pasted on sheets of paper, and given names which he

had himself coined.

Apart from the many botanical rambles he undertook in the vicinity of Llanrwst, he also records journeys which took him further afield. He once ascended Carnedd Llywelyn by starting up from Trefriw, climbing over Cefn Cyfarwydd and down to Cwm Cowlyd towards Afon Ddu. After crossing the hills between Pen Llithrig and Moel Eilio he descended into Cwm Eigiau where he saw an abundance of trout in Afon Porth llwyd. On reaching Cedryn farmhouse he was invited in and given a drink of buttermilk before starting on the final stage of the walk to the summit. He names the various plants seen on the way among which were the heath rush (*Juncus squarrosus*) and the different species of heather which had sheets of a white flowered variety. The woolly-haired moss (*Racomitrium lanuginosum*) which grows in luxuriant patches among the rocks and heather also caught the keen eye of the young botanist, and there follows a short but interesting note on the ecology of the plant. J. Lloyd Williams returned home from Carnedd Llywelyn by descending into Cwm Dulyn from where he made his way down to Llanbedr y Cennin before continuing his way home to Llanrwst through Talybont and Trefriw.

He climbed Tryfan for the first time when he was twelve years of age. J. Lloyd Williams had been sent to Bethesda to represent the family at a funeral there. While walking along the road which passes beneath the mountain an argument developed between Williams and the friend who accompanied him, concerning the two boulders which stand on the summit. In order to settle the disagreement it was decided to climb Tryfan on the way back from Bethesda and find out if the two figures on the summit were indeed two carved statues as the friend had claimed. Tryfan was climbed from the western side and on gaining the summit Lloyd Williams scrambled to the top of one of the two boulders, known as 'Adam and Eve', and leapt from one to the other. The Capel Curig road was regained by scrambling down the precipitous eastern side of the mountain, where he discovered a rare alpine hawkweed (*Hieracium holosericeum*).

Years later, while he was based at Bangor, Lloyd Williams was able to spend more time botanizing in the Ogwen district. During one of these visits he had arranged to meet an Oxford Professor in order to show him one of the localities of the Snowdon lily (*Lloydia serotina*). Lloyd Williams cycled to Ogwen from Bangor, while the Oxford man arrived in a closed carriage; his main ambition was to see as many rare plants as he could growing in their natural habitats. The visitor, on stepping out of his carriage, promptly inquired as to the site of the Snowdon lily and Williams replied by pointing to the Glyder cliffs which were at the time partly obscured by dark clouds. One look at the dark glowering cliffs caused the visiting botanist to change his mind, and he quickly stepped back into his carriage, promising to return the following June. The don, true to his word returned the following year and, with Williams leading the way, they set off for the mountains on a clear sunny morning. The visitor wore smooth soled leather boots which presented problems whilst climbing up steep grassy slopes, but otherwise all was going well until they arrived at the last stage of the journey, just below the '*Lloydia*' site. This final pitch consisted of a steep slope of short grass, loose stones and exposed soil. Here the don stopped and nervously announced that he could go no further. Seeing that they were only a few feet from the Snowdon lily Lloyd Wiliams tried to persuade his accomplice to carry on, to which after several minutes of discussion, the don reluctantly agreed. The locality was finally reached after Williams had helped the terrified visitor along, creeping on all fours and clinging to anything that he could grasp, but he refused to open his eyes when he arrived at the base of the cliffs. This meant that he did not see the '*Lloydia*' and Lloyd Williams removed one plant out of the dozen or so that were within easy reach, and placed it in his pocket. The pair then made their way slowly and carefully down from the base of the cliffs, the don gradually regaining his composure once an easier path was reached. Within days the story was spreading around Oxford of a mad Welshman who had led an eminent Professor on a perilous expedition among the mountains to see a rare flower. The Snowdon lily however was one rare plant that the Professor did not actually see growing in its natural habitat.

John Lloyd Williams will be remembered in botanical circles for his discovery of the rare Killarney fern (*Trichomanes speciosum*) on Moel Hebog in 1887, but before continuing with that account it will be of interest to the reader to learn something of the history of this very special plant.

The Killarney fern was first discovered in Britain by Dr Richard Richardson (1663-1741) at a site near Bingley in Yorkshire. The specimen he gathered was later preserved among Uvedale's plants in the Sloane Herbarium housed in the British Museum. On the strength of a specimen gathered by Richardson 'at Belbank, scarce half a mile from Bingley, at the head of a remarkable spring', the record was published in the 1724 edition of John Ray's *Synopsis*.

Information regarding the exact localities of this fern were kept secret by those who knew them for fear of the plant becoming extinct due to over collecting. This actually happened at a site in the Harlech area, and could well have been the case with the old Snowdon locality, where once the finest colony in Britain grew. The mystery and romance surrounding the rare plant localities were much coveted by the plant hunters and added much to their enjoyment during the great Victorian collecting era. A similar sense of achievement is experienced by present day field botanists when during the course of a day's excursion a new locality for a plant is discovered; the main difference between them and their forerunners being that the camera has replaced the vasculum as a vital part of the botanist's equipment. The feeling of satisfaction however remains the same.

133

The first discovery of the Killarney fern in Wales was made by J.F. Rowbotham of Manchester in 1863. The exact locality is not given apart from the fact that it was found 'in a part of the Snowdon range'. The following description of the site appears in the *Journal of Botany*, 1, 1863, in a note by Thomas Moore who had been corresponding with Rowbotham regarding the discovery. 'I found it in a large hole formed by fallen rocks alongside a cascade of water; and admission to this hole, which is about five feet high by four feet wide, is obstructed after a depth of about three feet by this Fern falling from the rocks at the top, and growing out of the sides in the form of a beautiful curtain, down which the water is constantly trickling; the whole having much the appearance of a crystal screen'. The fronds were described as being 'abundant and remarkably fine', and, 'quite equal to the bulk of the Irish specimens in luxuriance of development'. (The south western counties of Ireland are in fact the stronghold of the plant). One specimen gathered by Rowbotham measured 22 inches in overall length. In 1864 the Botanical Society of Edinburgh received Killarney fern specimens from nurseryman James Backhouse Jnr., which he claimed to have gathered in Caernarfonshire. No more details of the exact locality were given but it is believed that the fronds came from the same site as that described by Rowbotham. The name of Backhouse appears on several Killarney fern records from North Wales, as well as from other parts of Britain during the period in question; these are viewed with scepticism by some as the Backhouses, being nurserymen, would have had access to the finest Irish specimens, and the deliberate introduction of species to the wild was not unknown. On the other hand, one of the Killarney fern sites of North Wales was shown by Backhouse to local botanist D.A. Jones of Harlech who later recorded the incident in his manuscript flora of Meirionnydd.

Williams Williams (1805-1861) the Botanical Guide was rumoured to have planted Irish specimens of the Killarney fern in the Snowdon district prior to the discovery made by Rowbotham in 1863, and James Britten (1846-1924) who was aware of this claimed that the fern was known by some to grow in two localities in Caernarfonshire as far back as the 1830s. Britten prepared a list of plants for publication in *Jenkinson's Practical Guide to North Wales* in 1878 and has this to say on the Killarney fern. 'This rare and beautiful fern exists in the Snowdon district; but the exact locality is known to very few, and is wisely kept concealed'. Charles Babington records in his journal an entry dated 17 July 1832 that he spent the day examining the rocks in the vicinity of Dolbadarn Castle near Llanberis in a vain attempt to find the Killarney fern that had been mentioned as growing there.

Rowbotham's locality remains a mystery to this day. There have been no reports of the fern having been seen on the Snowdon range of mountains since Sir John Bretland Farmer, writing on the flora of the region in Carr and

William Williams The Botanical Guide:
(note the plant collectors Vasculum in the background)
Courtesy Gwynedd Archives

Lister's *Mountains of Snowdonia*, (pub. 1925 and 1948) claims to have known one Killarney fern locality in the Cwmglas area for more than twenty years.

J. Lloyd Williams published a note in the *Journal of Botany* (London:25,p.215) recording his discovery of a Killarney fern colony on Moel

Hebog, near Beddgelert in 1887, but refrains from divulging even the name of the mountain. 'In July last I found a very good specimen of Trichomanes radicans [Killarney fern] growing in a damp hole near the top of a range of mountains. Not knowing the locality in which this fern was discovered before, I cannot guarantee but that this one is identical with it, and for the same reason as that which induced the locality reported in 1865 to be kept secret, I must take the same precaution in this case. I may state, however, that it was not found on any part of Snowdon. I took a small portion of the fern and planted it, but left the greater part of it behind'.

Williams made this discovery during his years as a young headmaster at the Garn Dolbenmaen school and gives a vivid account in his autobiography (Williams 1945) of an incident which resulted in the colony being temporarily eradicated. On his return to the village that evening he informed a friend of the discovery he had just made, adding that a good sum of money could be made from the find should a greedy plant hunter ever come to hear of it. He returned to the site a few weeks later to find the damp hole stripped clean of all vegetation; not a frond was left. Williams visited the locality several times before leaving Garn Dolbenmaen in 1893 but found no trace of any regeneration of the fern. Twenty four years later he again returned to Moel Hebog, this time with a group of botanists who were interested in ferns. Williams arrived at the pre-arranged meeting place half an hour before the others and decided to pay a quick visit to the old Killarney fern site, out of curiosity, before the others came. He was delighted to find that the fern had recovered in its damp rocky recess, and after picking one frond from the clone returned to the meeting place to greet the others. He showed the specimen to the visitors, but not the locality. The party spent the remainder of the day botanizing in the Moel Hebog area, but not one of the visitors discovered the fern, and Lloyd Williams did not show it to them either.

The site however was known to at least one other local botanist prior to its discovery by J. Lloyd Williams. In an article on ferns which appeared in the Welsh journal *Cymru* (June 1921) the Reverend Thomas Pritchard Edwards (1853-1922) gives a fascinating account of how he discovered the Killarney fern on Moel Hebog about two months before the site was found by Lloyd Williams. Edwards decided to keep quiet about the discovery and did not visit the site again for two years. So concerned was he over the safety of the rarity that he decided on this occasion to make his way to the locality by taking an indirect route over the mountain with an occasional glance behind to make sure no one was following. On arrival however, he was dismayed to find the recess stripped completely bare.

Edwards' claim to be the first to discover the Killarney fern site on Moel Hebog is substantiated by the fact that he published details of the locality, plus the story of the fern being removed, in 1921, twenty-four years before

Williams publicised his own account in the fourth volume of his autobiography. Both botanists give a similar description of the site; a small damp rocky recess above which grew the tuft of hart's-tongue fern (*Phyllitis scolopendrium*) which first aroused their curiosity and induced closer inspection. In the concluding part of his article Edwards recalls a conversation he had with J. Lloyd Williams at an eisteddfod some ten — fifteen years later. The subject being discussed was the recently published *Flora of Anglesey and Carnarvonshire* by J.E. Griffith to which Lloyd Williams had contributed a substantial list of south-Caernarfonshire plants. During the course of the conversation Edwards asked Lloyd Williams if J.E. Griffith had ever seen the Killarney fern site on Moel Hebog. The latter replied by saying that he did not believe Griffith had ever seen the locality for himself but that he had informed him of where the fern used to grow prior to the destruction of the colony.

Griffith had included the Killarney fern in his *Flora* with the following appended note: 'I have seen this fern growing, undoubtedly wild, in one place only. This was first found by Mr J. Lloyd Williams. I refrain from giving the locality as it is so rare!' This presents an inconsistency which is based upon the fact that there is in the Herbarium at the Department of Botany, National Museum of Wales, Cardiff, a specimen of Killarney fern measuring six inches in length (including the stipe) which was collected by J.E. Griffith from Moel Hebog in 1891. One can therefore but assume that Lloyd Williams is mistaken when he states that the fern had not reappeared between 1887 and 1893, but it must be remembered that the account was written over fifty years after the events took place. A more recently typed note attached to Griffith's Herbarium sheet suggest the existence of another site of this plant in the same area and this adds to the mystery which still surrounds the Killarney fern in Snowdonia. The note reads:

> 'Trichomanes radicans: [Killarney fern *Trichomanes speciosum*]
> Seen on Garn Dolbenmaen, Moel Hebog, by A.H. Trow in the company of J. Lloyd Williams: fronds described as being two feet long. Date not stated.
> Recorded from conversation.
> 1st December, 1937.
>
> H.A.H.' [Dr Harold Augustus Hyde (1892-1973)]

It is encouraging to know that attitudes have changed considerably towards plants in recent times and this fern is now protected in Britain under the Wildlife and Countryside Act of 1981. It is equally encouraging to know that the Killarney fern, despite the depradations it suffered during the Victorian era, is known by the writer to be extant in two sites within the boundaries of the Snowdonia National Park and that recent studies undertaken by Dr F. Rumsey of the Natural History Museum, resulted in the finding of an abundance of the gametophytes of this plant in North Wales.

John Edwards Griffith was born in 1843 the son of Griffith Griffith, Taldrwst, Llangristiolus, Anglesey. He was apprenticed at his uncle's chemist shop in High Street, Bangor, taking over the business in 1864 when his uncle died. Griffith was married to Ann, the daughter of Rowland Parry, Fron Heulog, Bangor, who died in 1888. He was shortly to re-marry Ellen Augusta, the only daughter of the Reverend John Williams Ellis of Glasfryn, Llangybi and Plas Lodwig, Bangor. He gave up the chemist business shortly after re-marrying, spending the remainder of his life as a gentleman of private means.

In addition to his botanical work he also wrote the *Portfolio of Photographs of Cromlechs* (1900) and *Pedigrees of Anglesey and Carnarvonshire Families* (1914). Griffith studied the plants of Anglesey and Caernarfonshire for twenty years prior to the publication of his *Flora* of the two counties in 1894/5. He had already published a shorter version of this work fifteen years previously by instalments which appeared in the *Naturalist*, the journal of the Yorkshire Naturalists Society; this formed the basis of his major work. Griffith's personal copy of the *Flora* is kept at the Bangor City Library. This volume has been re-bound and interleaved with blank pages, these having been used by the author to note additional records which he had amassed over a thirty year period following the publication of the original work. The *Flora* included 1119 species of flowering plants and 219 varieties of which nine species and varieties were, at the time, new to science, and seventeen species and varieties, new to the British flora.

J.E. Griffith is remembered mainly for his work in compiling his *Pedigrees of Anglesey and Carnarvonshire Families* (1914) but among his many interests were archeology, antiquities, and photography as well as botany. He was also a J.P. and a director of the Bangor Market Company. He died at Bryn Dinas, Bangor in July 1933, aged 90, and was buried at Glanadda Cemetary.

John Lloyd Williams was the chief contributor to Griffith's *Flora*, supplying records of 81 flowering plants and 14 ferns. He was a botanist of the old school and was in his element when on a botanical excursion among his beloved Snowdonian hills. This interest never left him; even when he was fast approaching his 90th birthday he visited Cadair Idris to see once more a rare plant he knew since the days of youth. He died aged 91 at Bath, Somerset, on 15 November 1945.

Thomas Pritchard Edwards was a native of Caerwys in Flintshire as his literary pseudonym 'Caerwyson' suggests. He served as an Independent minister at Llanrwst and later with the Wesleyans at Blaenau Ffestiniog where he was also the editor of the local newspaper *Rhedegydd* from 1899 until 1906. Edwards edited a guide book for Blaenau Ffestiniog in 1911 in which he included a note on the botany of the district.

John Edwards Griffith (1843-1933)

He spent the last part of his life at Arenig near Bala where he died on 4 March 1922 being buried at Capel Celyn in the cemetary which now lies beneath the waters of Llyn Tryweryn.

The Golden Age of the Mountain Guide

During the early period of the mountain guides, the service was provided on a part time basis. However, by the end of the 18th century the demand had increased to such an extent that Edmund Hyde Hall, writing during the years between 1809 and 1811 describes Snowdon thus: 'This mountain is throughout the summer a source of considerable revenue to the adjacent villages, where reside the guides to whose care strangers commit themselves in order to visit the peak'. With the coming of the slate and copper industries more families began to move into the area and among them were men who were willing to act as guides to parties of visitors who wanted to ascend Snowdon. Unfortunately, only a small minority, it would seem, took the trouble to get to know more than simply the way up and down Snowdon from Llanberis. In an article which appeared in the *Gwyliedydd*, in 1830, [see *Hynafiaethau a Thraddodiadau plwyf Llanberis a'r Amgylchoedd* by W. Williams, 1892, p.61] the writer has this to say on the matter: 'Mae yn ofynol bod yr arweinydd yn Sais a Chymro da, ac yn hynafiaethydd geirwir. Bu amryw wyr dysgedig ym mhen y Wyddfa, ac arweinydd gyda phob un, ac a ysgrifenasant enwau llynau, mynyddau, a dyffrynau, yn ôl a ddywedai yr arweinydd . . . Ond erbyn i'r cyfryw foneddigion gydmaru eu llyfrau, nodai un Foel Eilio yn sefyll ar y de, a Charnedd Llewelyn yn y gorllewin o ben y Wyddfa; a nodai llyfr arall hwynt yn debyg i'r modd y maent, ac nis gwyddid pa un i'w goelio . . . Mae yna ugeiniau yn ddigon cyfarwydd a'r ffordd i ben y Wyddfa; ond heb ychwaneg na hyny, nis gwnant ond twyllo boneddigion am eu harian a'u llafur'. (The guide should be fluent in both English and Welsh and also be a reliable antiquarian. Many learned gentlemen have ascended Snowdon accompanied by a guide and wrote down names of lakes, mountains and valleys according to what was said by their guide, but on comparing their books these gentlemen found that one noted that Moel Eilio stood to the south, and Carnedd Llywelyn to the west of Snowdon; while another book noted them in their true positions, so that it was not known which to believe . . . There are scores who know the way up Snowdon but no more than that, so that they only defraud gentlemen of their money and toil.)

The 19th century saw the opening of more and modern hotels in Capel Curig, Llanberis and Beddgelert, and the services of mountain guides could be hired in all of them. Evan Jones of the Capel Curig Inn was a harpist as well as a guide, and he also undertook the duties of barber and waiter. Like most of the 'reliable and intelligent guides' he had an interest in botany and minerology.

The most famous of the Capel Curig guides was Robin Hughes. According to the 1861 census returns he was 62 years of age, married with 2 sons and lived at number 5 Yard Newydd, Capel Curig. It is interesting to note that the entry under the occupation column describes him as a 'Guide to the Snowdonian

Prince Llewelyn Hotel, Beddgelert

Hills', which suggests that by the mid 19th century the once part-time
occupation of guiding had developed into a vocation that provided a living
wage.

Robin Hughes was 61 when he guided John Tyndall, the famous alpine
mountaineer and scientist, up Snowdon from Gorffwysfa (now Pen y Pass) in
1860. Tyndall, despite his Alpine experience, had arrived in the area on a
snowy December day rather ill prepared for a winter assault on Snowdon, but
they managed to gain the summit despite having to wade through drifts of soft
snow. Tyndall, with his friend Huxley, had brought no ice axes or gaiters with
them. They bought two rake handles at a shop in Bethesda, while on their way
from Bangor to Capel Curig, and had the local blacksmith fit them with rings
and iron spikes. During the ascent Tyndall complained of numbness in the feet
as the result of his boots becoming filled with snow due to the absence of
gaiters.

'The guide,' wrote Tyndall, 'though he acquitted himself admirably during
the day, had at first no notion that we should reach the summit; and this made
him careless of preserving himself at the outset. Toning him down a little, we
went forward at a calmer pace.'

Robin Hughes was also known to that renowned angler and hill walker John
Henry Cliffe and in his book *Notes and Recollections of an Angler* (1860) pays

141

tribute to him as 'the celebrated Capel Curig guide'. Hughes took great delight in relating to his clients the legends and folkore of Snowdonia and also accounts of his own experiences among the hills. Cliffe and Robin Hughes were once caught in a storm whilst traversing the Glyder from Cwm Idwal over to Llanberis and the author gives the following account of their time spent sheltering in the inn at Nant Peris.

'On arriving at Llanberis, we were glad to seek the nearest shelter and speedily found ourselves before a roaring peat fire discussing the merits of a jug of excellent cwrw, and rude entertainment as the "public" afforded. Here we were detained several hours; our guide in the meanwhile amusing us with a detail of sundry adventures he had met with in the mountains. Our host was a Yorkshire miner; he had migrated hither forty years before, married a Welsh girl, and in short had become so completely forgetful of "fatherland" as to speak his own native language very imperfectly. He had, in fact, been completely transformed into a Welshman in everything except his appearance, which retained unmistakeable evidence of his Saxon or Danish origin. Our homeward journey to Capel Curig was performed in the dark, and with plenty of wind and rain to add to our discomfort; we afterwards regretted that we did not remain at our humble quarters and "rough" it through the night'.

Robin Hughes held the greatest respect for Richard Edwards, the Beddgelert man who was known as 'the father of Guides'. Richard Edwards was older than Robin Hughes, and the hard life of the mountain guide was beginning to take its toll on the veteran by the time that Thomas Roscoe visited North Wales. During this visit Roscoe climbed Snowdon under the guidance of Robin Hughes and they met Richard Edwards near the summit. Roscoe records: 'it was a cordial meeting, and seemed to give equal pleasure to both. The old guide shook him [Robin Hughes] heartily by the hand and regretted that he now saw him so seldom. I am breaking fast, Robin, [said Richard Edwards] and you will see less of me soon'. Robin Hughes replied by saying that he looked well, but added 'these hard up and down trips are enough to break any body, let alone one of your years. It is time for you to turn gardener, like my father, and leave this work to the ponies and the easy-chairs — all the fashion now!'

Richard Edwards lived at a place called Pen Bont Fach, which used to stand close to the present site of the Prince Llewelyn Hotel. He also officiated as parish clerk for a time and was instrumental in placing the memorial slab which marks the grave of Gelert, the legendary hound of Prince Llywelyn. (Jenkins 1899 p69). In 1832 Richard Edwards and Robin Hughes formed a search party when a visitor called Philip Homer was lost on Moel Siabod. Details of this incident appear in Thomas Roscoe's *Wanderings and Excursions in North Wales* (1836) as was related to the author by Robin Hughes, but not all the facts were published at the time. There are, however, among the manuscript notes of

" -Richard Edwards. The Snowdon Guide "

Died March 19. 1845
aged 74.

Richard Edwards: 'The Father of Guides'
(Photo: National Library of Wales)

another tourist, the Reverend John Parker (1833) an entry which gives a much clearer account of the events leading to the tragic death of the young visitor.

'Friday 21 June. Heard this evening the account of Mr Homer's death near Capel Curig last November. Mr Homer was considered as partially deranged, and set out from his Hotel (the Inn at Capel Curig) with a Lieutenant . . . whom he quitted very shortly, saying that he should go to the summit of Moel Siabod. He borrowed a pair of gloves which were afterwards found on top of that mountain. As night came on, Mr Homer's absence caused some alarm at the Inn, and on the following days much anxiety was felt as to the cause of it. In the course of about a fortnight, however, his corpse was discovered under a shelving rock that is in sight of Llyn Gwynant, on the rugged slope above the lake. The weather had been foggy with snow, and his path was traced for some distance on Moel Siabod but his body was only found by accident. The poor fellow did not seem to have received any outward injury but his death seemed rather to have arisen from cold and hunger. He could hardly have lost his way for the road was in sight and houses were I believe in view, but he had collected from distance places heaps of rushes and fern with some stones and of these materials he had made a rude shelter in addition to the natural rock which overhung them. The body had not begun to decay, his feet were without his stockings and placed in his hat round which he had also bound a part of his coat, and every circumstance appeared unaccountably perplexing. Mr Homer had received a classical education and was the son of a Tutor at Rugby. His death I imagine to have been caused by eccentric and imprudent exposure to cold accompanied by a sudden and fatal exhaustion'.

Richard Edwards died 19 March 1845 aged 74.

Another well known Beddgelert character who operated as a Snowdon guide was Evan Thomas who lived outside the village in a cottage near Cae'r Gors two miles along the Caernarfon road. He also worked in one of the Aberglaslyn Coppermines, being a typical example of the part time Snowdonian guides of the period. The following paragraph quoted from the 1825 edition of Whittaker's *Cambrian Tourist or Post-Chaise Companion through Wales* gives a vivid interpretation of the guide's personality plus an interesting description of his home.

'We engaged the miner as our conductor over the mountain, who entertained us much with displaying, in strong colours, the tricks and impositions of his brother guides, and more particularly of the methodistical landlord of our inn, who is generally employed on these occasions. His pride, too, is not a little elevated, by having conducted the Great Doctor to its highest summit; this seeming ridiculous phrase for some time puzzled us; but we have since found out, that our guide was talking of no less a man, than the present respectable and learned Dean of Christchurch, who ascended this mountain last year. Though our guide was pompous, and rather too partial to the marvellous, yet I strenuously recommend him to all Tourists. At half past twelve, we started from our inn, determined to see the sun rise from its highest summit. The night was now very dark, and we could just discover, that the top of Snowdon was entirely enveloped in a thick impenetrable mist: this unpropitious omen staggered our resolutions; and we for some time hesitated respecting our farther progress; but our guide assuring us that his comfortable cottage was not far distant, we again plucked up resolution; and, quitting the high way about two miles on the Caernarvon road, we turned to the right, through a boggy, unpleasant land, and in danger of losing our shoes every step we took. This soon brought us to the comfortable cot, the filth and dirtiness of which can better be imagined than described; a worm-eaten bed, two small stools, and a table fixed to the wall, composed the whole of his furniture; two fighting cocks were perched on a beam, which Thomas seemed to pride himself in the possession of: the smoke of the fire ascended through a small hole in the roof of this comfortable mansion, the door of which did not appear proof against the 'churlish chiding of the winter blast'. Such, indeed, was the situation of this Cambrian mountaineer: and, though, in our own opinion, misery, poverty, and dirt personified, seemed to be the real inhabitants of this cottage, yet there was something prepossessing in his character; for frequently, with the greatest vehemence imaginable, and in the true style of an auchorite, he declared, that, 'though he boasted not riches, yet he boasted of independence; and though he possessed not wealth, yet he possessed the home of happiness, an honest breast.'

By the mid 19th century the Snowdonian Guides were carrying pocket books which they used as testimonials. On returning from a trip the client would be requested to enter down in the guide's pocket book any comment he wished to make. The entries made in these pocket books invariably begin with the time taken to reach the summit, followed by the weather conditions with regards to the views they had, and conclude by giving praise to the guide. The pocket book would then be used by the guide as a testimonial which he could show to future potential clients.

Thomas Jones hailed from the parish of Penmorfa and he most probably moved to Beddgelert soon after he got married. The 1861 census returns show that he was a widower living with his daughter in Church Street. His personal pocket book which is kept at University College of Wales, Bangor, measures 6½ inches by 4, and is dated 1845 to 1849. It is evident from the entries in the pocket book that Thomas Jones conducted some very important people to the summit during his career. One entry from July 1846 states: 'Lord Lewisham has known Thomas Jones for some time and has great pleasure in recommending him as an excellent guide in every respect. He is always cheerful and extremely civil besides knowing the neighbourhood thoroughly'. R.W. Long, writing of his tour through North Wales in 1847, had this to say: 'Our Guide was Thomas Jones, a man of Swiss-like appearance who might have been a Mont Blanc Guide from his looks. He told us that an old gentleman whom from his description I recognized to be Sir Henry de la Beche (having seen his name in the Hotel book at Llanberis) had been in the neighbourhood several days persuing his geological researches. He said he had been a Guide to a Grand Duke and the King of Saxony'. Sir Henry De la Beche (1796-1855) was Founder and Director of the Museum of Geology.

At the end of the pocket book several notes have been written in Welsh explaining the procedure followed during an inquest, and this sudden interest was no doubt sparked off by the disappearance of the Reverend Henry Wellington Starr of Northampton while attempting to climb Snowdon alone on a misty day in September, 1846. Starr's body was not found until June of the following year and the circumstances which surrounded his death aroused suspicions of foul play. This unfortunately created an atmosphere of suspicion and rumour among the local inhabitants and the guides suffered more than anyone. Starr arrived at Caernarfon on the afternoon of Monday 14 September and after acquiring a room at a lodging house in Pool Street, had retired early to bed. The next morning he informed his landlady that he was setting out for Llanberis, Snowdon and Beddgelert and would later return for his luggage and letters. He took with him a small oilskin knapsack containing a change of linen, but never returned. Meanwhile his mother and sister were daily expecting a reply to their letters, and on receiving none, made enquiries to Mr Pritchard the Postmaster at Caernarfon. The reply they received did not alleviate their worries. All the letters they had sent were still at the post office in Caernarfon waiting to be collected.

Mrs Starr and her daughter Emily immediately started out for North Wales and after arriving at Caernarfon went straight to the lodging house in Pool Street where the Rev. Starr had been staying. After gleaning from the landlady what information she had, they took a post-chaise to Llanberis and began their inquiries at the Dolbadarn Inn. Mrs Evans the landlady there remembered a gentleman of Starr's description arriving who had slept there on the Tuesday night, but left the next morning in the direction of the Llanberis Pass, apparently to ascend Snowdon. On the assumption that he had reached the summit and had signed the visitors book kept there, a guide was immediately dispatched to fetch it down, but on inspection his name was not there. The next morning a guide called John Hughes stated that he had met with a gentleman answering to the description of Starr on the Glyder mountain on Wednesday, 16 September between 5 and 6 o'clock in the evening. The guide described in detail the man's height, and manner of attire, and said that he wore only one glove. He went on to say that the gentleman had told him that he was a clergyman and had come from Llanberis, over Snowdon, past the coppermines and then continued on up the Glyder. He added that he had accompanied the gentleman some distance down the Glyder to make sure that he avoided a dangerous precipice, and had then returned to his young son who he had left in charge of some crystals they had collected on the mountain that day. Later, while examining the contents of Starr's carpet bag and great coat at Caernarfon an odd glove was found which substantiated the relevance of Hughes' previous account of the gentleman he had met with on the Glyder.

Another guide then claimed to have seen Starr, this time on the opposite side of Snowdon. Robert Owen, guide and landlord of the Snowdon Inn, near Llyn Cwellyn claimed to have seen Starr sitting and smoking his pipe on the bridge at the upper end of the lake between 4 and 5 o'clock on the afternoon of Tuesday 15 September. When Starr enquired of Robert Owen the route to Snowdon he was adviced by the guide not to go on account of the mist that hung over the mountain at that time. Starr however insisted on going and was later said to have been seen by two farm hands working near Llyn Ffynnon y Gwas.

As the mystery surrounding Starr's disappearance continued several unsuccessful searches had been made. Posters, giving a description of him, were distributed and a £50 reward was offered to anyone who could find him. At one stage over 900 men from the Dinorwig Slate Quarries combed the slopes of Glyder and Snowdon in a vain attempt to solve the mystery. Soon afterwards the snows of winter postponed any further searches that year.

On Monday 1 June 1847 William Hughes, a huntsman was descending the vale of Cwmbrwynog when he picked up a red shawl at the foot of the precipice of Moel Cynghorion and took it immediately to the Dolbadarn Inn where Mrs Evans identified it as that of the Rev. Starr. It was also then revealed that the oilskin knapsack of Starr had been found a month previously. On the Tuesday William Hughes, together with Edward Humphreys of the Dolbadarn (Mrs Evans' son in law) returned to Moel Cynghorion and searched the area around the spot where the shawl had been found. They later found the remains of the unfortunate tourist and various articles which were afterwards identified as belonging to him. The remains were conveyed to the Dolbadarn Inn and on Monday 7 June an inquest was held before the Coroner E.G. Powell. Emily, Starr's sister, attended the hearing in order to identify the property found, and John Evans, who found the oilskin knapsack, and William Hughes the huntsman were also questioned. When John Evans was asked why he waited a month before reporting the finding of the knapsack he replied that he had heard that the missing Starr had been seen in Ireland. The Coroner did not think that the testimony of the guides John Hughes and Robert Owen worth hearing, and they were not called upon to testify.

One guide, however, was called upon to give evidence and he was William Williams (1805-1861) of the Royal Victoria Hotel. Williams, a native of Rhuthun had moved to Llanberis in 1832 to work as a 'boot-boy', hence his nick-name 'Will Boots'. He came to Llanberis during the heyday of the great Victorian collecting era, and when he first began to act as a mountain guide he was a keen collector of crystals and insects. When the first huts were built on the summit of Snowdon in 1837 or 1838 Williams went into partnership with Morris Williams of Amlwch, a copperminer who first had the idea of providing refreshments on the summit. William Williams, in an attempt to add to the attraction of Snowdon 'dressed himself in a suit of goat-skin, consisting of cap, coat and trousers, which made him appear like a savage from the land of perpetual snow . . . the flocking visitors soon made the humble summit a paying concern'. William Williams presumably left the business soon afterwards and Morris sold his share to his brother Phillip Williams who subsequently formed a partnership with John Roberts the guide, mentioned in the previous chapter. In due course there were two separately run huts providing refreshments for tourists on the summit. John Roberts managed the hut belonging to the Royal Victoria while William Roberts, another guide, looked after the interests of the Dolbadarn Inn.

William Williams was familiar with the localities of the rare plants of the district, and came to be known as 'the Botanical Guide', with a special interest in the rarer ferns. He occasionally ascended Snowdon three times in one day, including a night ascent; the custom of going up to watch the sunrise was popular then. Williams became well known among the leading botanists of the day and benefited from his specialist knowledge when the collecting of ferns

147

developed into a craze. Charles Cardale Babington (1808-1895) Professor of Botany at Cambridge and Edward Newman (1801-1876), an authority on ferns, both knew Williams well and in Newman's book *A History of British Ferns*, he is described as 'an active and intelligent Snowdon guide, ... well acquainted with the Snowdonian stations of both the Woodsias:' (the two rare ferns *Woodsia alpina* and *Woodsia ilvensis*) who was 'subject to constant solicitations from botanical tourists to be conducted to the localities . . . ' Charles Babington, writing in August 1857, (U.C.N.W. Pamplin Letters, August 1857) credits Williams with the discovery of the rare mountain avens (*Dryas octopetala*) in Snowdonia. The plant still grows on high rocks above Llyn Idwal where the old guide first found it and it was the only known locality for it in the area until the late Evan Roberts of Capel Curig (N.C.C. Head Warden) discovered another locality on the Carneddau in 1946.

James Britten (1846-1924; Assistant, Botany Dept., British Museum, Nat. History) writing in the *Jenkinson's Practical Guide to North Wales* (1878) page lxxxix, notes the probability of the mountain avens (*Dryas octopetala*) having been planted at the Cwm Idwal site.

There is strong evidence to suggest that Williams was concerned for the future of the rare plants and would only show the localities to those whom he trusted. He once got into an argument with a Cambridge botanist called Barton over the identification of a rare fern and during this incident the visitor accuses Williams of deliberately misleading him, an accusation later published in the *Phytologist*, a popular botanical journal of the time. Barton, with his friend, had ascended Snowdon from Beddgelert and had seen Williams in one of the summit huts. The guide had come up from Llanberis along the Pony track with a client to see the sunrise. Later, while Barton and his friend were coming down they saw Williams climbing on the cliffs of Clogwyn y Garnedd. 'We had little doubt,' says Barton, 'that he was engaged in a search after some rare plants, as he had the reputation of being well acquainted with almost every inch of the whole Snowdon district.' Williams approached them with a fine specimen of holly fern (*Polystichum lonchitis*) which he had just gathered from the heights above. During the conversation which followed, the guide agreed to show the alpine woodsia (*Woodsia alpina*) to the visitors, but Barton disagreed with Williams on the identity of the fern in question. It seems that Williams lost his patience with Barton after this incident, and he led the party away from his favourite hunting ground of Clogwyn y Garnedd and up the steep slope of Carnedd Ugain, along the ridge to Bwlch Coch and down through Cwmglas Mawr to the Llanberis Pass. Barton claims in his letter that Williams deliberately misled him during his quest for a specimen of the alpine woodsia (*Woodsia alpina*). Babington on the other hand has a high opinion of the guide and states. 'I believe the man to be honest and well intending,' before concluding by saying that 'exterpation is the rule in Wales with tourists and collectors who call themselves botanists.' William Williams was quite an original character with a flair for gaining publicity and wore a fur cap bearing the words 'Botanist Guide' in bold letters. The following lines which were sent for publication to the North Wales Chronicle a short time after his death is said to be the guide's own work.

'William Williams, guide to Snowdon,
Anxious that all those who 'bode in
England, Scotland, or old Ireland,
Should place their feet upon much higher land
Than ever was in those parts seen
By young or old that e're have been,
Gives notice, that if here they'll ride,
He, with much pleasure as their guide,
Will show them quarries, lakes, and mines,
Snowdon, and the place he finds,
Plants that nowhere else abound,
And which by him alone are found:-
Waterfalls with various actions,
Minerals, ores, and pertifactions;
The house where Margaret Evan died,
St Perry's well and all beside:
Anglers too, who with a boat
Can be supplied and when afloat,
Will find at once by asking him,
The places where the best trout swim;
In fact to him, no place is new,
Within the range of Snowdon view
Excepting one, which he declares
To bring folks to he never dares,
Not being on the best of terms
With him who owns these hot concerns,
'The Devil's Kitchen', it is named,
And by some tourists is much famed;
'Tis here we're told, the king satanic
Allures his own by means botanic,
But there are guides who know it true,
Its inmost parts and master too,
And folks who wish to go with these,
Can walk the road with greatest ease;
To guide elsewhere, 'midst many millions,
There's none so good as William Williams'.

(N.W. Cronicle, 29 June 1861)

William Williams became a legend in the Snowdon district and 'Llyn Wil Boots' (Will Boots' lake) used to be a well known landmark at Llanberis, now vanished under the village by-pass. Williams was beginning to realize that the plants were being gathered to the point of near extinction, and that he would be as guilty as anyone if they disappeared. Babington, Pamplin, and other prominent botanists were also aware of what was happening, but the collecting went on. Williams began to construct a small lake at a site below the old Goodmans Quarry near Llanberis. In this lake he planned to build small islands, where he could transplant the rarities, out of reach of the greedy plant collectors. This then was 'Llyn Wil Boots'. Had the dream of establishing a haven for the rare plants of Eryri been realized, then it would have been the first nature reserve if its kind in Snowdonia, and perhaps in Wales.

Despite these conservationist ideals which he undertook at Llanberis, it was all very inconsistent with what he got up to on the cliffs of Snowdon. The following account is but one example.

William Bennett (1804-1873), a London botanist, visited the Snowdon district in 1849 and hired one of the younger guides to take him to Clogwyn Du'r Arddu, and after collecting several specimens of the more common ferns they continued on towards the summit of Snowdon. They met William Williams near Bwlch Glas and immediately began to badger him for specimens of the alpine woodsia (*Woodsia alpina*). The 'Botanical Guide' took the visitors to the edge of the precipice and there pointed out to them 'the exact spot where the Woodsia grew, far down amid a world of rocks and precipices'. Williams knew well enough that the visitors would never find the fern, and on departing promised to mail a specimen to them should they fail. The vistors went down from Bwlch Glas, heading in the direction pointed out to them earlier by Williams. They searched among the rocks as best they could, finding holly fern (*Polystichum lonchitis*), but failed to find the *Woodsia*. On arriving at the summit later that day they found that the guides in the huts there were selling Holly fern for sixpence a root, but they knew nothing of the *Woodsia*. William Williams, true to his promise, posted to Bennett some fronds of the alpine woodsia and these packets can now be seen at the Natural History Museum, London.

At the time of the disappearance of Starr, Williams assisted a certain Mr Johnstone of the Royal Victoria Hotel move from Llanberis to Chester, and he did not return to Llanberis until the day after the body was found. Williams told the jury at the inquest of how he was informed by Mrs Evans of the Dolbadarn Inn of William Hughes' discovery, and that on the following morning he walked over to the Snowdon Inn at Betws Garmon to pay ten shillings that was part of a twenty-two shilling debt that he owed there since the previous year. He continued: 'On my return I took the direction of the mountain where the remains were discovered, and found a piece of linen near the place; I saw a string hanging to it, and placing my foot upon the linen, I drew the string out. It had the appearance of a watchguard; and on opening the folds of the linen I found the watch'. Williams kept the watch, and did not hand it over to the authorities until later; for this he was repremanded by the Coroner for 'conucting himself as to create a suspicion on his integrity'. The jury returned after a few minutes consultation and announced: 'That the Rev. Henry Wellington Starr, in the month of September last, was ascending a certain mountain in the said county, and died on the same, without any hurt or injury having been done to or committed upon him by any person or persons whatsoever; but the said jurors are unable to state whether his death was occasioned by a fall, by cold, or how otherwise in particular, although they incline to the belief that it was caused by his accidentally falling over a precipice, during the hours of darkness'. The death of Starr was still shrouded in mystery, and certain suspicions pointed to the finder of the watch, William Williams. The watch, upon examination was found to be quite free of rust or moisture, and in perfect working order, despite the fact that, if Williams' story is to be believed, it had been out on the mountain from September until June. It could therefore be assumed that Williams had found Starr's body soon after he died and had taken the watch. It should also be noted that when Williams, several years later, related the story of how he found the watch to a visitor called Wynter, he said that he had spent a week on the mountain searching before he found it.

Emily Starr, who later published an account of the events leading up to the tragic death of her brother has this to say in conclusion. 'That the Welsh be jealous for the honour of their country, and greatly attached to their mountainous principality, is both natural and just; and it must be evident to all who have read the account of the inquest, that the chief endeavour was to do away with any stigma attaching to their character, from the mysterious disappearance of a traveller among them.' All this happened at a time when the tourist industry was expanding rapidly in Snowdonia, businessmen were investing heavily in expanding the railways and in building larger hotels, and therefore any suspicions as to the safety of the tourist had to be permanently removed.

It is ironic that William Williams met his death on his favourite fern-hunting cliff. He attended service at Jerusalem, the independent Chapel at Llanberis on the Sunday before his fatal accident where a collection was made to help a poor widow. Williams donated a half-crown and a penny. The collector, thinking that a mistake had been made, called Williams' attention to the money on the plate, but the old guide said it was all right. It appeared afterwards that he had given all the money he had. At 10.30 a.m. on the morning of 13 June 1861, Williams set out from the village of Llanberis to conduct a lady and a gentleman to the summit of Snowdon, and down to Beddgelert. During the course of the ascent Williams left the couple to go and collect plants, and rejoined them later on. After reaching the summit he left them again, this time to collect specimens of alpine ferns for his clients. On this occasion he failed to return. Meanwhile his clients, who had been waiting for him in one of the summit huts decided to continue their journey guideless to

Beddgelert. Word soon got around about Williams' disappearance and subsequently a search party was organized. His body was later found at the foot of a gully on Clogwyn y Garnedd. This gully is known to this day as Will Boots' Gully and a small rock of quartz was placed at the point from which he fell. The accident occured as a result of a broken rope. His tombstone at the old Churchyard in Nant Peris bears a fitting epitaph to the man.

UNDERNEATH
LIE THE REMAINS OF
WILLIAM WILLIAMS
UPWARDS OF TWENTY FIVE
YEARS BOTANICAL GUIDE AT
THE ROYAL VICTORIA HOTEL
WHO WAS KILLED BY A FALL
FROM CLOGWYN Y GARNEDD
JUNE 13 1861 WHILST PURSUING
HIS FAVOURITE VOCATION

This Tomb Stone was erected to
his memory by a few friends.

It also stands as a memorial to all the Snowdon Guides; men who played such an important part in the history of Snowdonia.

William E. Powell was the first to arrive at the scene of William Williams' death on Clogwyn y Garnedd in 1861. Powell, otherwise known as Gwilym Eryri, was at the time working in the nearby Snowdon coppermine, but had also been a guide during which time he was responsible for one of the summit huts called 'Hotels' by the Victorians.

He was born in Cae'r Bompren, Beddgelert on 20 February 1841, the son of Evan and Sian Powell. He was also employed for a time at the Brynfelin coppermine near Aberglaslyn where he was promoted steward and addressed as Captain Powell as was the industry's custom. In 1865 he married Jane, the daughter of Rhys and Margaret Roberts, Bwlch Mwrchan, Nantgwynant, and in the following year they emigrated to the United States of America settling at Milwaukee, Wisconsin. Powell found employment with the 'Chicago and St Paul's Railroad Company' being appointed in 1878 as general emigration officer. He was to lead many a family overland to settle in the rich lands of Dakota and one town there bears his name: 'Powell'.

Being possessed of a likeable and helpful personality he soon became a prominent figure among the Welsh community of the United States. He was a poet, musician and contributed a number of articles for the journals, *Drych* and *Columbia*. He died 1 December 1910 aged 69 and was buried at Forest Home, Milwaukee.

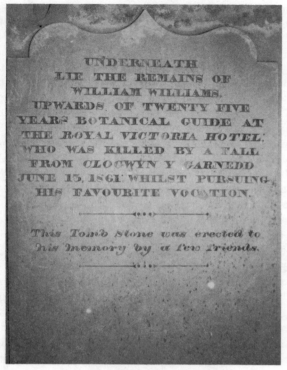

Tombstone of William Williams
at Nant Peris Churchyard

William Roberts operated as a guide from the Dolbadarn Hotel at Llanberis. According to the 1861 census returns he was a 39 year old married man with four children. During the 1850s a traveller by the name of William F. Peacock visited North Wales and later published details of his tour in a book entitled *The Welsh Mountains &c.* This portrait of William Roberts the guide is quoted in its entirety from that printed work.

'The guide Roberts' costume is rather picturesque and very slightly savouring of Switzerland; that is to say made up of light trousers, ditto vest (both fawn colour), no coat; the vest having long arms, and fitting to the person. A brigandish hat on his head, a knapsack or large wallet on his shoulder (well strapped over the chest), and a stout stick in his hand, which is (to crib a bit of our allies tongue) literally his 'baton' of office. Such is honest William Roberts; a civil quiet, well-informed fellow, who respects an agreement, and can be thankful for favours conferred on him; who rejoices to be guide when anybody wants to be guided, and (in time of dearth) pursues cheerfully his work as a labourer. I have real respect for Dolbadarn Roberts and Dolgelly Pugh (of whom anon, when we ascend Cader Idris). William's memory holds many a curious legend and he loves to satisfy your questions, though he rarely speaks unless spoken to. Like most other guides he carries the bottles of the party; ensconces them in the capacious stomach of his wallet. Let the tourist who thinks to ascend Snowdon engage Roberts, honest Roberts; I say this with ingenuousness, for it's not a matter of 'commission'! The best recommendation is, that he has gone up and over above 2,000 times in twenty-five years of his professional life.'

There is a memorial slab on the wall inside the Church at Beddgelert to the most successful of all the Snowdon guides. Harry Owen was born at Castell, a farm on the slopes which rise above Llyn Dinas near Beddgelert. On 8 May 1847, when 25 years of age he married Ann Pritchard, who was at the time in service at nearby Plas Gwynant. Owen had already purchased the inn at Pen y gwryd together with some adjoining land before his marriage, and the couple ran the business for a period of over forty years. They had ten children, but two of these died in their infancy. There were five sons, namely Harry, John, Owen, Griffith and Hugh, and three daughters, Catherine, Jane and Annie. Under the care of Harry Owen, Pen y gwryd Inn was established as a centre from which early mountaineering in Snowdonia was to develop. As the fame of the inn and its keeper spread, so did the demand for his services to guide parties to the mountains or to hire one of the rowing boats which he kept for the use of visiting anglers.

Harry Owen seems to have shared the same ideals as Robin Hughes of Capel Curig in encouraging and developing new routes up the mountains. The following is quoted from an old Capel Curig Inn visitor's book; a rare mention of the innkeeper in action as a guide. '28 June 1865. Ascended from Pen y gwryd by an unusual track under the summit of Clogwyn y Garnedd — thick mist — no view . . . Henry Owen, Guide.' Pen y gwryd Inn was ideally situated as a base for climbing, walking, botanizing and fishing among the mountains of Snowdonia. Horse drawn carriages were also available to convey visitors further afield to such attractions as the Swallow Falls or Betws-y-coed. The house of Harry Owen became increasingly popular with mountaineers; details of their adventures being duly recorded in the famous 'locked book' which was later reflected in the numerous published guide books to every crag in Snowdonia and beyond.

On 8 January 1803 a piece of land called Weirglodd Goch, near Betws Garmon was leased to John Morton of Caernarfon by the landowner Sir Robert Williams of Plas y Nant, and soon after the Snowdon Inn was built. John Morton adopted the name 'Snowdon Ranger' and began to guide visitors up Snowdon from his house. The term 'Snowdon Ranger', however dates from an earlier period. In the 16th century Snowdon was part of the Royal Forest of Snowdon, and the Earl of Leicester held the office of chief ranger of Snowdon Forest during this period. The lease was transferred on 12 December 1812 to John Morgan, Cae Darby, Caernarfon and Ellis Roberts of Beddgelert for a further period of 21 years.

Evidence of Robert Owen being the landlord of the Snowdon Inn appears in the Quarter Sessions Records for 1815 in which the following is stated. 'Recognizance document, . . . Henry Williams of Drws y Coed went surety for £5:0:0 for Robert Owen Glanllyn Cwellyn to appear at the next Quarter Sessions'. The nature of Robert Owen's offence is not mentioned apart from the fact that it was committed against an Elizabeth Williams. A year later a similar document dated 16 December records, 'Mem. of Recognizance of Robert Owen of the Snowdon Ranger, pa Betws Garmon, victualler, for £10, Thomas Hughes of Glanrafon, farmer for £5 and Henry Williams of Drws y Coed, farmer, for £5 for the appearance of R.O. at the next Quarter Sessions and to keep the peace, esp. towards John Morgan of Waunfawr'. Again, details of the offence are not given.

It will be remembered also that Robert Owen claimed to having seen Rev. Starr on the bridge near Llyn Cwellyn on the day of his disappearance in September 1846. When George Borrow visited North Wales in 1854, it was probably Robert Owen who introduced himself to him as the 'Snowdon Ranger', during the course of their conversation outside the Snowdon Inn. Borrow describes him as an elderly man wearing a smock and a fur cap. Another traveller, who was looking for a guide to conduct him up Snowdon, saw him on the shores of Llyn Cwellyn hobbling about with the aid of two sticks. The prospect of 7/6, which he charged for his services, however, caused a miraculous change in him and he walked to his house with the 'alacrity of youth'. During the ascent, the old guide walked faster and firmer than any of the party. Robert Owen died in 1855 aged 71 and he was buried at Beddgelert. He had been operating as a Snowdon Guide for over 30 years.

In Europe, the Alpine guides were becoming organized. The Chamonix Corporation of Guides had been formed as early as 1823, the Oberland organization in 1856, and those in other parts of Switzerland shortly afterwards. It had become customary for guides to carry the pocket book or *fuehrerbüch* as the Swiss called them, during the 'forties and fifties', and as we have seen earlier, while discussing Thomas Jones of Beddgelert this custom was also practised in Snowdonia.

The pocket book of John Hughes of Llanberis, has been handed down in the family and is now in the possession of Owen George Hughes, his great grandson. The pocket book follows the same pattern as that of Thomas Jones of Beddgelert, and gives the date of the excursion, the name of the client, details of the route taken with reference to the views and weather conditions, and concludes with a few favourable words on the conduct of the guide. The inscription on the book gives Coed y Ddôl, Llanberis as his address, but the Census records him living in Goodman Street. He also worked as a slate quarryman and hairdresser; and the latter is proudly inscribed on the front page of the pocket book, the leather cover of which still bears the marks of where he sharpened his razor. John Hughes led parties of visitors around the slate quarries, as well as to the Glyder and Snowdon and the book contains several references commending the guide's botanical and geological knowledge. 'Sept 21 1871. I ascended Snowdon, descending via Capel Curig, under the guidance of John Hughes. I found him every way capable, and intelligent and possessed of a good knowledge of the geological formation of the region and of its botanical products'. John Hughes operated independently as a Snowdon Guide, and he kept a number of ponies for the use of those who wished to be conveyed less strenuously to the summit. The charge for the use of a pony was 5/-, but guides fees varied from village to village. The guides at Beddgelert charged 7/-, and if the party wished to continue their journey either to Llanberis or Capel Curig the fee was 10/-. A night ascent to Snowdon from Beddgelert also cost 10/- and the other prices were: Pen-y-gwryd = 5/-; Snowdon Ranger = 7/6 and Capel Curig = 10/-. There is an entry in John Hughes' book for 10 August 1868 which states that there were nine ponies in his charge that day and the guide's fee was 5/-. The client, believing this charge to be quite reasonable composed these lines for the guide's book:

'They recommend their civil guide
In whose conduct you may confide
He will take you up and down
And be contented with a Crown
But when you ride from Victoria's door
You must pay 2 shillings more.'

It is unlikely that the John Hughes in question was the same person as the guide of the same name who said he saw the Rev. Starr on the Glyder in 1846. The man on the Glyder had his son with him collecting crystals, whereas John Hughes' eldest son was not born until 1861.

Early in 1993 Gwynedd Archives Service purchased one of the visitors books which were kept in the Snowdon summit huts during the middle years of the 19th century. (G.A.S.XM/9254) On the pages of this most important manuscript are names, descriptions, drawings, poems and all manner of personal remarks which portray the everyday life on early Victorian Snowdon. Recorded also are the names of the guides which operated on Snowdon during the years 1847-48. Robin Hughes of Capel Curig and Thomas Jones of Beddgelert feature prominently in the book; the Capel Curig guide was renowned for pioneering new routes and for criticising those who rode up Snowdon on the easier paths. He once prophicised to Roscoe that 'a long winded pony-road, winding miles round, and as smooth as a railway' would someday be built from Capel Curig to the summit of Snowdon, 'and we might then go up Snowdon in an easy arm-chair after dinner!'

Another of the guides whose name is often mentioned in the book is Elias Roberts, who served the Royal Victoria Hotel at Llanberis. Elias Roberts was born in Amlwch, Anglesey in 1807 and was known locally as 'Lias bach'. In 1869 a bonfire was lit on the summit to celebrate the coming of age of the heir of the Vaynol Estate and Elias Roberts drove a horse and cart to the summit to carry a barrel of pitch for the bonfire, and this was the first record of a horse and cart being driven to the top of the mountain. He was nearly 80 years old when he died suddenly outside the post office at Llanberis. Other guides noted in the book are David Jones, host of the Prince Llewelyn Hotel, Beddgelert, Richard Owen of the Royal Victoria, Llanberis, Evan Watkins of Capel Curig and Thomas Roberts of Beddgelert; the latter tragically lost his life as the result of an accident which occurred as he returned to Beddgelert from Snowdon.

The conduct of these guides are mentioned in glowing terms, but there is one who failed to meet the standards set by the others. An entry for 11 June 1847 states as follows:

'J.W. Williams, Robert Marshall of Sheffield & Pryse Claridge of Aberystwyth ascended Snowdon one Sunday with Guide from Carnarvon and found him a dam' lazy fellow I could not get him along at all after the first mile. Mr J. Browne accompanied the lazy guide & thought himself a b'y fool for taking such trouble J.P. Hamer of Caernarvon says Jer. Bower of Liverpool'.

J.P. Hamer of Liverpool moved to Caernarfon during the 1840s and operated a guiding service to Snowdon from his office in Segontium Terrace. He advertised his service in a booklet of truly Victorian flavour that he published in 1850. In it he claims that the 'Hamer's Route' to the summit was shorter and easier than any other. Hamer's excursions to Snowdon started at 10:20 a.m. from Segontium Terrace and the parties were conveyed by carriage to the Snowdon Ranger Inn. 'Hamer's Route' followed for the most part the Snowdon Ranger path and the party stopped for a minute's rest out of each 10 minutes of walking. Hamer assured his clients that the summit would be reached after 2½ hours walking and that a clear view was 'all but certain'. After reaching the summit the party would sign the Hamer's Log before returning to the Snowdon Ranger Inn for a 'substantial tea' before returning to Caernarfon. The trip cost 10 shillings, but the business did not prosper; there is no other mention of Hamer in this, or any of the other Visitor's Books, and there is no trace of the 'Hamer's Log'.

Those who visited the Snowdon district regularly during the final decades of the 19th century would have been acquainted with the old guide Tom Ward. His passing would have gone unrecorded however had it not been for an accident he suffered when over 70 years of age; this was not an accident which occurred during a mountain ascent, but rather as the result of tripping over the shafts of a cart closer to home. As a result of his injuries he was admitted to the hospital connected with the workhouse at Caernarfon (now known as Eryri Hospital) where a local newspaper reporter found him and published his recollections in the *Herald Cymraeg*, of 28 February 1911.

Ward moved from his native Headon, Nottingham to Llanberis at an early age. He was employed as a messenger boy at the local Post Office in addition to being a guide and led several prominent people to the summit of Snowdon during his career. Among those which he named were Tennyson and John Ruskin, the latter's philosophy often quoted by Ward to visitors who complained of the weather, namely that there was never any bad weather on Snowdon, only different varieties of the fair.

The injured guide claimed to have ascended Snowdon over 4,000 times using five different routes and covering a distance of 30,000 miles; he longed to be sufficiently recovered so that he could return to his beloved mountain once more. Ward's dislike of trains is made clear by him during his interview with the reporter stating that he had only twice made any rail journeys, the farthest that he had travelled being from Llanberis to Caernarfon, and many people having never before seen him in any conveyance came up and asked him what was wrong.

His interests, apart from walking also included geology and botany, and when asked about the dangers of mountaineering he replied by saying that it was no more so than playing soccer providing that the necessary care and precaution was applied. He concluded that mountain walking provided the best course of exercise that the human body could have, and that many still preferred to walk up Snowdon rather than use the train, a development that had greatly affected his business and no doubt re-kindled his great dislike of trains.

It is not known if Ward ever regained a state of fitness which permitted him to continue his chosen profession; the coming of the train caused a severe depletion among the numbers of the Llanberis guides, but at least one of their ilk is known to have successfully moved with the times by being employed as a conductor and porter by the 'Snowdon Tramroad and Hotels Company Limited'. 'Owen Glas', as he was known, continued to pass on to his passengers in the confines of the carriages the local knowledge that he had previously related to his clients in the open air during his guiding days.

Tourism increased in Snowdonia with the expansion of the railway system. The line between Caernarfon and Llanberis was opened in 1869, and visitors arriving at Llanberis Station would see there a row of sturdy mountain ponies and a guide ready to convey them up Snowdon. The following years saw an increase in the number of young men and boys willing to act as guides and there were instances of touting for business among them. Over the years the paths had become easier to follow, and better maps and guide books were published. In 1896 the prophecy of Robin Hughes became reality when the Snowdon Mountain Railway was opened, and this heralded the end for the guides of Llanberis. In 1937 a popular guide book writer asked if there are any mountain guides left in Snowdonia? 'The routes are so well marked and cairned that there is no doubt about presence and direction, and it is rare that you come across a party with a mountain pony ridden by a lady.' The age of the Snowdon Guide was over.

Bibliography

Printed Books

Aikin, Arthur *Journal of a Tour through North Wales* (1797)

Babington, Charles Cardale *Memorials Journal and Botanical Correspondence of Charles Cardale Babington* (1897)

Bingley, William *North Wales including its Scenery, Antiquities, Customs &c* (1804)

Borrow, George *Wild Wales* (Collins n.d.)

Bowen, Geraint (pub) *Y Traddodiad Rhyddiaith* (1970) "William Salesbury — ei fywyd a'i weithiau" gan W. Alun Mathias

Carneddog *Cerddi Eryri* (1927) [p20-21 re W.E. Powell, guide]

Cash, James *Where there's a Will there's a Way* (1873)

Clark, Ronald *The Early Alpine Guides* (1949)

Cliffe, John Henry *Notes and Recollections of an Angler* (1860)

Craddock, J [?] *Letters from Snowdon* (1770)

Davies, Hugh *Welsh Botanology* (1813)

Desmond, Ray *Dictionary of British and Irish Botanists and Horticulturists* (1977)

Ellis, Gwynn *Plant Hunting in Wales* (reprints from 'Amgueddfa' Bulletin of the National Museum of Wales; nos 10 Spring 1972, 13 Spring 1973, 16 Spring 1974)

Evans, Rev. J *A Tour through part of North Wales* (1802)

Forrest, H.E. *The Vertebrate Fauna of North Wales* (1907)

Glenn, T.A. *Family of Griffith of Garn and Plas Newydd* (1925)

Griffith, J.E. *The Flora of Anglesey and Carnarvonshire* (1894/95)

Gunther, R.T. *Life and Letters of Edward Lhuyd* (1945)

Hoare, D.L.F. *Snowdon — That Most Celebrated Hill* (1987)

Hobley, W. *Hanes Methodistiaid Arfon* 'Ardaloedd Waenfawr a Beddgelert' (MCMXiii)

Hucks, J. *A Pedestrian Tour through North Wales* (1979)

Hughes, W.J. *Wales and the Welsh in English Literature* (1924)

Humphreys, H. (pub) *Guide to the Summit of Snowdon* (circa 1850)

Hyde, H.A. *Samuel Brewer's Diary* (1931; reprinted from the B.E.C. Report for 1930)

Hyde Hall, Edmund *A Description of Caernarvonshire 1809-1811* (1952)

Jenkins, D.E. *Beddgelert, Its Facts Fairies and Folklore* (1899)

Johnson, Thomas *The Itinerary of a Botanist* (1908) Translated portion of *Mercurii Botanici* (MDCXLi)

Jones, Carey *Y Llanc o Lan Conwy* (1990)

Jones, Dewi *Tywysyddion Eryri* (1993)

Nicholson, G. (ed) *The Cambrian Traveller's Guide* (1813)

Owen, Bob *Diwydiannau Coll* (1943)
Palmer, William T. *Odd Corners in North Wales* (5th ed. 1948)
Peacock, William F. *The Welsh Mountains &c* (1855)
Pennant, Thomas *Tours in Wales* (John Rhys ed. 1883)
Raven, Charles E. *John Ray Naturalist* (Cambridge Science Classics series 1986)
Roberts, Brynley F. *Edward Lhuyd, The Making of a Scientist* (1980)
Roberts, Evan Stanton *Llysieulyfr Meddyginiaethol a briodolir i William Salesbury* (1916)
Roberts, Janet D. *O Ben Llŷn i Lle bu Lleu* (1985)
The Cambrian Tourist or Post-Chaise Companion through Wales (1825)
Thorne, R.G. *The History of Parliament* (1986) "The House of Commons 1790-1820" vi Members G-P
Turner, Dawson (pub) *Extracts from the Literary and Scientific Correspondence of Richard Richardson M.D., F.R.S.* (1835)
Tyndall, John *Hours of Exercise in the Alps* (N.Y. ed 1899)
Wiliam, Parch. Dafydd Wyn *Cofiant Wiliam Morris* (1985)
Williams, John *Faunula Grustensis* (1830)
Williams, J. Lloyd *Atgofion Tri-Chwarter Canrif* (cyf. 1-4, 1941-45)
Williams, Rev. P.B. *The tourist's Guide through the County of Carnarvon* (1821)
Williams, William *Hynafiaethau a Thraddodiadau plwyf Llanberis a'r Amgylchoedd* (1892)
Withering, William *Arrangement of British Plants* (vols 1-4, 1796)
Wyndham, Henry Penruddocke *A Tour through Monmouthshire and Wales* (2nd ed. 1781)

Newspapers and Journals

Awel Eryri (1907) Ysgrifau William Williams, Tregof, Llanberis

Anglesey Antiquarian Society and Field Club Transactions (1961) "Hugh Davies the Anglesey Botanist" by Thomas J. Owen.

Bye-gones (1893 Nov. 22) "John Williams of Llanrwst" by John Williams

Caernarvonshire Historical Society Transactions (Vol. 16, 1955 vol. 17, 1956) "Some Account of the Botanical Exploration of Caernarvonshire" by P.W. Carter.

Ceninen Gwyl Ddewi (rhif 1 cyf. xxxiv tud. 26) John Williams, Awdur 'Y *Faunula Grustensis*' gan T. Llechid Jones.

Caernarvon and Denbigh Herald (10 Oct. 1846; 12 June 1847; 5 May 1849) re Rev. Starr.

Climbers Club Journal (Dec. 1901) "Reminiscences of Pen y Gwryd" by C.E. Mathews.

Cylchgrawn Llyfrgell Genedlaethol Cymru (xvii, rhif 1, Haf 1971) "Llythyrau John Lloyd at Edward Lhuyd" gan Bryn Roberts

Cymru (Mehefin 1921) "Hamddenau ym myd Adar a Rhedyn" gan 'Caerwyson'

Fern Gazette (vol. 12 part 1 1979) "The Killarney Fern, *Trichomanes speciosum*, in Wales" by R.H. Roberts

Herald Cymraeg (3 July 1888; 28 Feb. 1911)

Journal of Botany (1905) "Lightfoot's Visit to North Wales in 1773" by Rev. H.J. Riddelsdell

Journal of Botany (61, 1923) "*Lloydia serotina*" by James Britten F.L.S.

Naturalist (1887 pp 181-190) "The Early Botanical Work of the late William Wilson" by James Cash

Proceedings of the Linnean Society (vol. 164, 1953) "Edward Morgan and the Westminster Physic Garden" by R.H. Jeffers

Proceedings of the Linnean Society (vol. 168, 1957) "A further note on Edward Morgan and the Westminster Physic Garden" by R.H. Jeffers

The Lancet (vol. 1, 1849) Notice of Dr John Roberts

The National Library of Wales Journal (xvii) "A New Account of Snowdonia, 1693, written for Edward Lhuyd" by Frank Emery

The North Western Naturalist (vol. xxi) "John Lloyd Williams" by P.W. Carter and A.A. Dallman

The Phytologist (1858 and 1861) re William Williams the guide

Y Casglwr (rhif 31, Mawrth 1987) "Rhamant y Rhedyn" gan Dewi Jones

Y Ford Gron (Awst 1933 td 221-222) "Cripian ar ôl Lili Eryri" gan Dr J. Lloyd Williams

Y Geninen (Ionawr 1917, rhif 1, cyf. xxv td. 117-8) "Richard Roberts, Melin y Coed, Llanrwst" gan William Williams

GENERAL INDEX

INDEX TO PLANT NAMES